Heathcote Williams was born
He is the author of *The Local*
at the Traverse, Edinburgh,
the Royal Court Theatre Lond
Court Theatre), which won him the 1970 *Evening
Standard* Drama Award as 'Most Promising
Playwright', *Malatesta, Remember the Truth Dentist,
The Supernatural Family, Hancock's Last Half Hour,
Playpen, Carnival of Cretins, The Immortalist,* (first
presented Oval House, Kennington), and *What the
Dickens! – Charles Dickens's Christmas Conjuring
Caper.* He is also a published poet.

MacGuinness

Axel Ney Hoch

Webster

Van Dyn

HEATHCOTE WILLIAMS

The Speakers

I have often listened to these speakers, and have
sometimes wondered where they came from, how
they lived, and where they would go when they
had said or screamed their say, and the gates of the
park were closing.

Sean O'Casey

ROBIN CLARK

Published by Robin Clark Limited 1982
A member of the Namara Group
27 Goodge Street, London W1P 1FD

First published in hardcover in Great Britain by
Hutchinson & Co. (Publishers) Ltd, 1964

Copyright © Heathcote Williams 1964

ISBN 0 86072 062 4

Printed in Great Britain
by Nene Litho and bound by Woolnough Bookbinding
both of Wellingborough, Northants

Contents

All photographs by Stephen Fry with the
exception of Webster which is by Jay Maisel

So many people now, Cafferty, so many
ignorant, illogical, boring people forced to
register their private decay.

The Park

THE LARGE group under the trees have not noticed that there is no one speaking at the centre, until two pairs of policemen enter the park and start to break up the meetings.

Lomas observes that they travel in pairs because they are neurotic. If they travelled alone, they would start talking to themselves.

Freddie Kilennen walks up to a pair and asks them whether they would like to take part in the première trial run of his pneumatometer, which is a machine for measuring how much of the Holy Ghost there's left in a man's soul, and he belches.

One of the policemen says: Shut your mouth and clear out of the park . . . because *I* say so; and Cafferty observes that if you have a hat shaped like a bomb, egocentricity is rather out of place.

The police close Cumberland Gate and herd the people towards the other. Harry, Norman and the man with feathers in his hair wander about the tarmac unconsciously repeating themselves: the unconscious repetition which leads to neurosis. The neuroses will be sold to the tourists the next day.

The man with the silent message has left his platform, on which he stands saying nothing at all, and sits in the mirrored section of Fortes studying form:

7

... to spot a winner, he says, demands a rare constriction in the mind, a constriction in the colours in the street, a constriction in the typography of the *Sporting Life*, a constriction in the air you breathe ... never change your mind once you have, through your training, lapsed into this constriction, and you'll win ... you'll surely win.

Lomas comes over to him and observes that Saturday night in winter in the park, when only the regulars are there, is like the service of compline in preparation for communion next day.

The man with the silent message says: As Aristotle, the great Italian sculptor said, a man is a man for all that.

Harry goes back to Chiswick, Norman goes back to Shepherd's Bush, Lil goes back to Stepney, Aggie wanders through the streets buttonholing people until she comes to the tea stand in Covent Garden, and then buttonholing people until she comes to the tea stand at the end of Hungerford Lane, Solly Sachs takes his dog back to Notting Hill; a man helps the woman from the Catholic Evidence Guild to fit her platform into the platform rack behind the *New Inn*, the man with the silent message goes back alone to the North End Road, and Lomas, Cafferty and Freddie Kilennen walk back to Kilburn.

*   *   *   *   *

The next day the tarmac is bare save for one or two figures in front of the Town and County refreshment stall. They flick peanuts at the pigeons, read the Sunday papers, lean against the till and talk to the waitress.

He died right here in this park, one ˙of them says. That communist speaker, and from undernourishment. That's the way Bonar died. That's the way they all die ... undernourishment. AND he was a communist speaker ... they don't even do for their own what they say they're going to do for us ...

A few people hang about in the entrance of Lyons and outside the Odeon. They look up from time to time at the park, roll up their newspapers, beat the palms of their hands.

The first speaker arrives: Robert Mathews of the Coloured Workers Welfare Association. He buys a cup of tea, and then wanders back across the tarmac to fetch his platform, with his cracked bowler hat on one side of his head and his briefcase, tied onto his waistband, hanging round his knees.

The West Indian known as Jahweh arrives in his white coat, dabbling with the calico strings of his wooden harp. He stands by the gate, opens his hebrew bible and begins to chant from it. His mouth begins to lather, his ringleted hair shakes in the wind. He gathers a crowd.

Van Dyn comes in the East Gate dragging his tea chest. He sits down on it, sorts out his newspaper cuttings, and wanders across to the catering stall to buy a cup of tea with no milk and five lumps of sugar. He looks about for the police and tries to sell some handbills with his photograph on them. They advertise a selection of tattoo artists, none of whom ever tattooed Van Dyn. He walks back to the tea chest, stomping the discarded paper cups with his heels. He screeches, kicks an oil drum across the tarmac and starts his meeting.

The man with the silent message hooks a milk crate from under the refreshment stall with his umbrella, brings it into the open, mounts it and reads his newspaper.

Mathews returns, drinks his tea with both hands for he has no fingers, erects his platform, climbs up on it and knocks the board at the top of it with his stumps shouting: OPPOSITION! COME ON ... OPPOSITION! COME ON POOR WHITE BASTARD, POOR WHITE TRASH, COME ON ... OPPOSITION ... He gathers a crowd.

The park fills.

Platforms, notices and banners slowly rise above the heads of the listeners: THE END IS NIGH in slab letters on flapping sail cloth; THE COMMUNIST PARTY OF GREAT BRITAIN; THE PROTESTANT TRUTH SOCIETY; THE SALVATION ARMY; THE MOVEMENT FOR

FREEDOM IN KASHMIR; THE CATHOLIC EVIDENCE GUILD; THE MOVE-
MENT OF PAN-AFRICAN EXPONENTS AND OF PEOPLES OF AFRICAN
DESCENT, and beneath it: GIVE US THE LIBERTY TO KNOW, UTTER
AND TO ARGUE FREELY ACCORDING TO CONSCIENCE ABOVE ALL
LIBERTY; THE NATIONAL SECULAR SOCIETY; THE EX-SERVICE MOVE-
MENT FOR PEACE; THE NATURAL LAW RELIGION; POBLACHT OIBRITHE
IN EIREAN AR GCUSPOIR: THE CAUSE OF LABOUR IS THE CAUSE OF
IRELAND, written awkwardly on a board, the outside layer of
wood corrugated with the rain; THE SOCIETY FOR EVANGELIZING
LONDON; HOW THE WAR OFFICE ROBS INVENTORS; Stanley Broder's
INDIVIDUALISM; and then the faint syllogism of the Church Army:
GOD loves you. GOD wants you. YOU need God.

*   *   *   *   *

Lomas, Cafferty and Freddie Kilennen have been drinking in
the *New Inn* for a couple of hours:
Well, says Lomas at length, shall we do the rounds?
All right.
They get up, leave the pub, cross the Edgware Road and walk
down the subway until they come up into the park. They stand
in the crowd of the speaker nearest the park gate at the top of the
subway steps:
. . . if you search from now till you die, the speaker is saying,
you'll never find a man or a woman or a body of people that can
remedy the weakness in mankind, only GOD can do that.
There's plenty of evidence, my friends, plenty of evidence to
PROVE that you are weak, you have only to look around you
and see the stupid things that men do. HERE is a message which
tells you WHY human nature is weak, HERE is a message which
tells you in what way YOUR weak nature can be remedied,
not by a man, not by men; no, my friends, not even by a woman,
for this message was written in the very hand of God. It reassures
the soul seeker, it reassures the . . .

Faith can move mustard seeds, says Lomas.

Join the Roman Catholic Church for the bones with the soft centres, says Freddie Kilennen, if you can swallow the tale of the whale swallowing Jonah, you can swallow anything.

Another clergyman telling you how you can get V.D. off lavatory seats, says Cafferty. Let's move on.

No, wait a minute, says Lomas. When are you going to stop heckling and start speaking?

When are you? Cafferty says.

My speaking days are over, says Lomas.

They never began, says Freddie Kilennen.

They did . . . they did, Lomas says. Well, Cafferty?

I don't know.

Well, as I've told you before, there are a few speakers left that you should bear in mind before you speak; I don't say that you can learn anything from them, but you should bear them in mind. . . .

Which ones? Cafferty said.

The ones who've been coming here for fifteen years or more.

All right, said Cafferty, let's move.

They move across the tarmac to a crowd by the railings:

. . . no, I'm not a fascist, madam, the speaker is saying. When I talk of foreign bodies, I don't mean Jews, Negroes or Roman Catholics. I mean the paths, habits, positions in our society which push us back in the road of history, the road of human development. Hanging is a dirty thing. Is it worse to practise it in public when a vast majority of the people in this land and certainly in this park would adore it? It is assumed that their sensibilities and their stomachs wouldn't be able to stand the scene so it is conducted in private, wedged between carbolic tiles. I am not totally destructive. I do not want to abolish lamp posts. I WANT TO ABOLISH THE POISON IN THE POLITICAL BODY OF MANKIND . . . mankind is OVER FERTILE . . . mankind is . . .

That's Axel for you, Lomas says. He's been coming up here since nineteen forty three or four. Bear him in mind.

They find that the speaker behind them has moved his platform. The edges of the two crowds mingle. They turn round:

. . . the Irish are only mad because the English expect it of us, the speaker is saying. Now, I remember when I came over here to make my second million pound. I was young, well dressed, well fed and very highly sexed and I was walking down Greek Street, a notorious street for whores . . . this was the red lamp district and I was the light, and I was walking down this street straight over from Ireland when this girl comes up. She glides across the street in my direction and I hitched my eyes onto hers, and she skids to a halt . . .

MacGuinness, Lomas says.

Yes, Cafferty says, how long has he been coming up the park?

Well, says Lomas, he was known as the boy speaker just after the war. He's been coming up here seventeen, eighteen years.

The crowd pushes closer. They are hemmed in, and they struggle out to a more loosely knitted meeting.

. . . I KNEW he did, I KNEW he did, the speaker in this meeting is saying to a heckler. He's a real humanist, always giving away what he hasn't got, and now he wants to put shoes on footless children. He wouldn't put shoes on them if they had feet. Now before he got onto that he was on about the BRITISH FLAG. The BRITISH FLAG isn't British at all. One part of it belongs to the Scotch: the cross of St. ANDREW, and they're always trying to get OUT of Scotland. The other is the cross of St. PATRICK, and you won't find any Irishman living under THAT, and the other cross is the cross of St. GEORGE, and he wasn't an Englishman at all . . . the only cross the English understand is the double cross . . .

Usual drek, Lomas says. Webster's been speaking in this park off and on for nearly forty years, but I don't think I've spoken to him since the war. We came at about the same time, in the late twenties . . . haven't spoken to him for a long time now. Let's move.

What about Van Dyn? Cafferty says. Shall I bear him in mind as well?

Yes . . . yes, says Lomas. I haven't listened to him in five years. It's bound to be the same stuff.

They move back and walk slowly through Van Dyn's crowd: . . . in that sixty eight years I have spent thirty years in prisons all over the world: San Quentin, Bonamora, Sing Sing, Dartmoor, Central Prison Pretoria . . . I've been in prisons all over the world. I was in the death house for three years. THREE YEARS IN THE DEATH HOUSE OF SING SING waiting to die like a mad dog. Now I have no education. What education I have had I picked up in reformatory schools and prisons all over the world. And talking about being in prison I don't boast about it. I incidentally was in Oxford College and that's the god's truth. I was only there a minute and a half when the burglar alarm went off and I had to get the hell out of it. I could have been like you . . . I could have been like you . . .

Same old stuff, says Lomas, but bear them in mind. Let's move on.

All right, says Cafferty.

*   *   *   *   *

A crowd shifts. They find themselves in the centre of a ring of people staring at the man with feathers in his hair who is hopping on one leg, watching an imaginary race through a shredded newspaper and a paper cup with the bottom pushed out, each held at one eye, and commentating on the race in gibberish. His hair hangs over his collar, his face is peeling like distemper, and as he hops round the front of the meeting collecting money, his swinging coat tails fan out a foul stench from his body. Lomas and Cafferty move for the nearest gap, struggle through the crowd until they find an open space, and stop in it. There is another man above them on a platform:

. . . all these people, he is saying raucously, come here every Sunday to indulge in this . . . look at it, this medieval hooliganism, this bear baiting. Not only is the man inside the ring mad, but the people watching, they're mad. But they're madder, my friends, because they can HELP it. The person in the middle . . . person, I suppose, that man with feathers in his hair, he is to be pitied, he's a cretin, you see, an idiot. It is sad that after nearly a hundred years of compulsory education and socialist enlightenment that the centre of a metropolis that has produced and nurtured a list of the greatest thinkers, and a list, I might mention, which includes Karl Marx, who is buried here at Highgate cemetery, here in London . . . it is sad, as I say that it is reduced to this. People have got nothing better to do than to come up here to laugh and poke at lunatics like they did in the middle ages. Tormenting and chaining up lunatics was the only free education they used to get in the middle ages. Well, of course NOW we regard it as stupid and cruel, but here we are after hundreds of years of so-called progress. Almost all these people can read and write, you know, and add up a column of figures. They may get it wrong and they may not know the meaning of the words they read, but they're all what passes for literate. Here is our struggle in the Socialist Party of Great Britain, you see. We depend for the success of our message on people who are prepared to THINK. We cannot do what in Lenin's day the Bolsheviks would have done, that is to seize power by a minority, and then lead the majority of sheep into the promised land. You see, if we thought that could be done, then life would be much easier, you see. We could say, all right we'll PANDER to this mob of lunatic baiters . . . we'll PANDER to this mob of idiots tormenting idiots, which is all they are, but you see we want . . .

There is too much discussion, Lomas says turning to Cafferty.

But the implication of that is that there is not enough of something else, but I'm sure there's enough of that too. I'm going over to Lyons for a cup of tea, I think Freddie's gone over there. Are you coming?

All right, says Cafferty, and they walk through Cumberland Gate back to the subway. Lomas ignores the entreaties of the pamphleteers selling *Challenge*, *Direct Action*, *The Socialist Leader*, *Freedom*, *The Weekly People*, *The Soviet Weekly*, *The Irish Democrat* and *Solidarity*. Cafferty buys one and stuffs it in his pocket.

Freddie Kilennen is in Lyons. Lomas buys three teas and brings them over on a tray to a table in the corner at the end of the hall.

Is it played out again? says Freddie Kilennen.

It's played out, Lomas says. There's no one much left now.

Have you really no ambitions left as a speaker? says Freddie Kilennen for Cafferty's benefit.

I have no ambitions left as a speaker, Lomas says, stirring his tea quietly. I've told you before that I've no ambitions as a speaker. The park is a plaything now, a showpiece. I've told it you before. It's just a place where people who have been told at an early stage in their life that there was a place reserved for saying that sort of thing or doing that sort of thing, have come and said it or done it every Sunday of their lives. It's like the Hindus, clenching their fists until the finger nails grow through the backs of their hands . . . neurotic bigotry. It's a showcase for all the old myths such as individuality equals aggression, and that other individuals can be bred if you're aggressive; and that good is good, and that there's no chance of a contrast between economically good and psychologically good; and that even if you get as far as distinguishing conscience from consciousness, they're both vulgar. All the questions that anyone asks in the park are personalized, and then the speaker inverts them to jack up the idiocy of the questioner . . . and then there's the other myth, I mean it's harmless, but if you can see lunacy seeping out of the edges of all layers of society, the only position it can have to itself is the apex. Cafferty must become acquainted with some of these myths and a few of the reasons before he becomes a speaker . . .

There you have it, says Freddie Kilennen. The measured judgment of a seedy Belfast intellectual who's been flogging his ears to the highest bidder for thirty years.

And what have you been flogging? Lomas says.

Freddie Kilennen says nothing.

Then haven't you any, now that you've given up speaking? Cafferty says.

Haven't any what? says Lomas.

Ambition.

You're wrong, Lomas says. I want to rage through the world of romantic novelists with a vast pair of pliers, unflaring people's nostrils. Reason is an emotion for the sexless.

*   *   *   *   *

Cafferty goes back to the park. Harry comes into the park from the Bayswater Road, muttering to himself and from time to time dislodging a horsehair moustache, soaked in red ink; he clips it back under his nose with a bent hairpin. He carries along a large wooden crucifix hung with butcher's hooks with stale bread spiked at the ends, and quoit rings, rubber tubing, twigs, leaves, cotton reels and ribbons. It is called his Paternoster. He uses parts of it to stand on his head.

Harry walks carefully into the park and talks to his friends before looking round for a platform; he has something in his hand:

You can say that, yes Phil, you can say that. It's a coincidence. I agree. Now on that board, you see, that top board of the Paternoster, I'm going to put this to stand on my head with. It's not really relevant, but I walked up Shepherds Bush to Notting

Hill Gate. When I got to Notting Hill Gate, I found I'd dropped something, so when I got to Shepherds Bush, about where, would you say . . . past the station, right outside, coming this way, I looked in the gutter and found this . . .

He shows his friends a rubber plunger. They admire it.

Yes, Harry goes on, yes, and I picked it up, you see. I said that'll come in handy, you know, something like that. It was half past eight at night. Now you see, I got up here and looked in the gutter across the road and saw something, and as I got to it, I put my hand in my pocket like this, and I said, that's funny, I said, must I have lost it. NOW LOOK . . . you see, TWO OF THEM . . .

He shows them another identical rubber plunger. They admire it.

May I die a death of agony, Harry goes on, and I couldn't tell the ruddy difference. One was at Notting Hill Gate, the other was here. Now don't you think that was strange? Lifetime after lifetime and you couldn't pick two up. I wouldn't mind if it was a week later . . . you see, I wouldn't mind if it was the NEXT DAY . . .

A friend of his brings a milk crate over.

Thank you Bill, thanks very much.

He gets up on it and holds his Paternoster in front of him, presenting arms. He gathers a crowd:

Now, says Harry raising his voice, now none of you can startle me in any shape or form. I'm past that stage. I've got the ammunition, and when I've got the ammunition I clear the deck for action.

Now my capabilities are absolutely stupendous. I can stand on this Paternoster on my head, but I don't want anyone to suffer from ennui. I use what is called the ad captum dandum technique, which is equivocal and contains irony, and that's no bunkum, it's absolutely fair dinkum. It's not what you think, it's what other people think of you.

I am the plenipotentiary of the century, I am the interpolator of interpolators, and I am THE Messenger with THE message. I used to say I am A messenger with A message, but that doesn't express the reality. I am the numquam quod. That expresses the capacity. I don't know who the message is for. I've never opened it, so I don't know what's in it, and I don't care . . .

STAND ON YOUR HEAD.

Yes, says Harry, we'll put that on the agenda. Now, this is what I was going to say: USE THIS EXPRESSION, each one of you, to yourself: AS I SEE IT . . . AS I SEE IT. I don't know what the hell you see, but you're in it. When YOU put YOUR optics to the aperture, they're not my optics, are they? because I knew a bloke who put his optics to the aperture on London Bridge about forty five years ago when I was there, and he said: Go on, have a look while I drown myself; and he did. And another fellow I knew at the time, I remember it, he started to shout ALL LONDON IS BURNING DOWN, and all they'd done was to stick a lighted newspaper in front of his face . . .

STAND ON YOUR HEAD, WILL YOU.

Harry gets off the milk crate, unhooks the quoit rings from the Paternoster and arranges them on the ground.

You don't think I can do it, do you?

No, says the heckler, a tall richly dressed Irishman with ginger hair and a camel coat.

Listen, says Harry, if you paid me, I could stand on my head on the roof of the Cumberland Hotel . . . but we'll have it on another way: put five pounds down there, and I'll cover it.

I expect you will, says the heckler. STAND ON YOUR HEAD.

It doesn't matter, says Harry, it's a nil admirare with me. I'm astonished at nothing you bring up. That old priest last night . . . I said you can go down there, over there or up there, it's a nil admirare with me. He was Greek Orthodox Church.

Harry turns around with his umbrella at arm's length to clear a
space in the crowd, then he arranges the rubber plungers and the
top board of his Paternoster.

But the police have started their shift in the park. Van Dyn has
disappeared. One of them pushes his way through Harry's
crowd, followed by the Inspector.

I've told you before to keep that rubbish out of the park.

What rubbish? says Harry.

All this trash lying round here obstructing people's freedom of
movement.

This is my Paternoster, says Harry.

Call it what you like, it's not to be left lying around in this
park. It encourages people to deposit litter, and unless you put it
in the litter bin provided, you'll have to leave the park. You've
been in this park long enough not to need to be reminded of the
Hyde Park Regulations.

They leave. Harry gathers up his gear. The man with feathers
in his hair whispers in Harry's ear: if they summon you, do time.
It'll only be two days, come out Tuesday dinner time. Never pay
a fine, after forty nine, you can't do time. At forty eight you
can't wait.

Harry hitches the butcher's hooks into the buttonholes of his
coat, lifts the Paternoster on to his shoulder, and walks out of
Cumberland Gate. The man with feathers in his hair takes over
the platform and brings back the melting crowd:

ANYBODY WANT TO WHIP ME FOR TWO POUND?
ANYBODY WANT TO WHIP ME FOR TWO POUND?
Now a three year old is always better than a four year old. You
see, you've got your fetlocks, smithlocks, underlocks, double-
locks, overlocks and other locks . . . see what I mean? Nothing
makes sense in Hyde Park, we're all nut cases up here talking
whether it's rheumatism, communism, unimultilateralism, labourism, fascistism or any other ism. There's only one ism today,
and that's moneyism. All your ideas on isms you can stick up that

tree and put a paper under it . . . or put an atom bomb under it and burn it. ANYBODY WANT TO WHIP ME FOR TWO POUND?

*   *   *   *   *

Cafferty goes back to the *New Inn* to find Lomas and tell him about Harry and the police. Lomas is at the bar buying scotch; he brings it over to the table, shoots it into the beer glasses, and sits down, staring at his knackered shoes.

That's nothing, Lomas says, nothing at all. When I spoke for the syndicalists . . .

Oh yes, says Freddie Killenen.

Shut your face, Lomas says, you think you've heard it all, but you haven't. When I was speaking for them and the Jarrow hunger marchers came into this park, they had MOUNTED POLICE who thought of BATONING the crowds down . . . BATONING them, Cafferty, and people used to come into this park for weeks after with their arms in slings and their heads in plaster. They don't look vicious when you film them at three frames a second, but they were vicious enough; and if the unemployed weren't batoned every weekend, we felt swindled.

You always make the same mistake, Freddie. You always think you always think you've got a RIGHT of free speech in the park. You've got no such right, you never had one, and you never will have. The tradition of speaking in the park started when they had executions at Marble Arch, at Tyburn, and they allowed the bloke they were going to hang to say a few words before his time came to boost the circulation of the Newgate Calendar. ALLOWED . . . you see, on SUFFERANCE, and that's all it's been ever since. It's the same at Tower Hill, only you're allowed to take a collection there, which you're not in Hyde Park, because it's a royal park, or some drek.

You went into it very carefully when your case came up

just before the war, didn't you dear? says Freddie Kilennen.

Yes, says Lomas, yes, I did as a matter of fact.

What happened? says Cafferty.

Freddie Kilennen yawns, gets up and goes to the bar.

Well, says Lomas, that was when I got mixed up in a fight in the park. There aren't any now.

What happened? says Cafferty.

Well, Lomas says, the only time I've got involved in a fight through speaking in the park was when I accused a man of being a worker. He knocked me off the platform, so I let him have it and they took him out on a stretcher. But you see, Cafferty, I had to go into it all very carefully; you see, there's no English parallel of the Declaration of the Rights of Man, or the French Constitution of 1791 . . .

No? says Cafferty.

No. All you've got is a NEGATIVE right to free discussion. In other words you can shoot your mouth off about anything you like, but it's subject to the laws of defamation, blasphemy, sedition and so on. But the police haven't really done anything about them since they knocked off that bloke who used to butt people in the stomach when they were speaking, they used to call him the wrecker. I've forgotten his name, but they knocked him off for shooting his mouth off about Aggie . . . said he'd seen her blowing bubbles through her stigmata in Lyons.

Why did they knock Harry off then? says Cafferty.

Hyde Park Regulations, that's all they're interested in now, and if they can't get you on them, then they can knock you off for being mad. Oh, there's the Public Order Act; I forgot that. That gives them the right to prosecute for conduct liable to cause a breach of the peace, but that depends on the context. When I looked into it I found that there was an old case in Liverpool where a man called himself a crusader of Protestantism, dolled himself up with a crucifix, wound some sheep's droppings on a string round his neck and started slagging the Liverpool Irish

Catholics. Pier Head, I suppose it was, yes, Pier Head. We used to have the Downs, Bristol for speaking, and then Gaol Square, Glasgow, and the Bull Ring, Birmingham, but I suppose they've all gone now. . . . Anyhow, there was a fight, and the magistrates bound him over to keep the peace, because he said it was this man's fault that there was a fight, since he was shooting his mouth off in Liverpool which is full of Irish Catholics. But that couldn't happen in Hyde Park, because there's no context . . . I mean, you haven't got a lot of anything in particular, except lunatics.

This was yours wasn't it, Cafferty? Freddie Kilennen says, coming back from the bar.

Yes, says Cafferty, taking the drink.

On the other hand, Cafferty, Lomas goes on, when some of the old gang who've been coming up the park for years say that they fought for the right of free speech and now all these lunatics come into the park and abuse all they fought for, they're right in a way because they took the police to task in court and forced them to be more tolerant, in enforcing these laws about blasphemy and breach of the peace and so on. I mean, I can remember when they picked you off the platform for using the word bastard. Jenner was knocked off for it, I remember. So, it's quite natural that the old gang get annoyed with the lunatics, but other people's attitude has changed. You've got that fellow on the Freedom for Kashmir platform who can't find words expressive enough to describe how evil the British are. You've heard him? The British are evil, he says, the British are absolutely unspeakably evil for the very simple reason that they enjoy it when he tells them this. It's the simplest thing in the world now to come to Hyde Park and tear the British people to pieces, and nobody minds because most people in Hyde Park aren't British, and most of them who are British have masochistic tendencies. They like feeling the whip lash of the vociferous lower classes, and ex-colonials. It makes them feel powerful. It's a kind of dreamland, a late imperialism.

So, we can't kick the natives on the streets of Mombasa any more;
so, we can't kick the natives on the streets of Delhi any more, but,
at least we can have the pleasure of them coming all the way to
Hyde Park to tell us what a lot of bloody imperialists we USED
to be. . . .

What was the park like before the rot set in? says Cafferty.

It used to be very strict up here before, and they used to have all
the religious speakers over by the old refreshment stall, and then
the political ones at the other end and the lunatics in the middle.
Now they've rebuilt it, they're all over the place.

*   *   *   *   *

In the park MacGuinness has taken over the platform of the
man with feathers in his hair. He has just finished a meeting, but
the police are on his back and he can't take a collection.

Take them to the gates, says the man with feathers in his hair,
take them with you to the gates, like Bonar used to do, and
collect outside the gates. They can't do anything to you then.

That is not my policy, MacGuinness says. My policy is to beg
them rotten where they stand.

It is about half past seven now.

Ogilvie comes back into the park for his second meeting. He
starts talking to a small group of friends at the edge of the grass,
then he breaks off, fits up his platform and asks them whether
they wish to constitute the thin red line necessary for a meeting.
A few people come over from across the tarmac.

Practically everyone in this meeting this evening, Ogilvie says,
with perhaps the exception of myself, is quite unnecessary. That
sets the pace for the meeting this evening which is completely
hopeless. I don't want anyone coming here thinking they're going
to be cheered up, because they're not, and if you don't like it you
can go away, and relieve me of the pressure of talking to you.

Some of them go away.

Go off and listen to the religious speakers, Ogilvie goes on. They'll tell you that when you die things will be a little better somewhere else that they can't specify, and they'll drive you there and you'll find it full of communists trying to find out what paradise had before it was lost.

The purpose of this therefore is just to entertain you in a light-hearted manner on a planet that's doing nothing, that's disintegrating beneath you in a vast stellar occupation that is meaningless. Are you with me?

Yes, says a middle aged man, sympathetically.

Look mate, for Christ's sake shutup, because you're not likely to do anything calculated to help me. In a minute I'll ask for questions and you'll remain dumb . . . you won't put a question, and when I DON'T want a question trust you to open your bloody mouth as if it meant something which it doesn't. Now why don't you go away and give the other end of your anatomy a chance, and then I'll know what's happening. But stop trying to kid me on that something's happening to you intellectually. Nothing's happened to you intellectually since the day you got born when you should have been done in. You've been deliberately bred by the English to be a degraded carcase of energy . . .

Why don't you like me? says the middle aged man.

Why don't I like you? what is there to like about you? LIKE? I HATE THE SIGHT OF YOU.

That's good, says the middle aged man.

What's good about it?

It's good that you hate me, I must be of some importance to you, says the middle aged man.

IMPORTANCE? . . . IMPORTANCE? . . . nothing's IMPORTANT. You're just at the receiving end of my vast state of nothingness. Are there any questions?

An African at the fringe looks carefully at the people standing next to him and asks Ogilvie what he thinks of England, freedom and free speech:

Let me put you in the picture with regard to the English, Ogilvie says. THEY ARE THE MOST DIABOLICAL RACE OF BASTARDS THAT EVER WALKED ON TWO LEGS ... listen, sir, listen. I mean this. I'm saying it humorously otherwise I'll start the revolution by accident. The English people are the most obscene and indecent people ever allowed to live on the earth's surface by a god in his interests. When the English educated you, they educated you because they realized that you were a danger to them uneducated, so they therefore put you in a state of educational paralysis. The English are NICE, NICE ... now NICENESS is the Englishman in a state of suspended animation. They have sold this idea to you, I can see it: you have that curious look on your face which the English employ when they are playing cricket. You are now therefore NICE. You're no longer a danger to them. You speak ENGLISH. You're just as confused as them by the bloody language they use. Listen, sir, listen. Do you understand the meaning of the phrase FREE SPEECH? Do you? You do ... what does FREE SPEECH mean? ... the gentleman down here says that free speech is the right to say what you want to say, when you want to say it, with regard to what is affecting you. It's a LIE ... it's a LIE. The English by free speech mean that state of insanity when what you say means nothing, and as soon as you say that it means something, they arrest you as an agitator. When the English talk about freedom, they mean freedom for the ruling classes of Britain and they mean enforced slavery for all those idiots who've been educated to think they're free when they're not. The English idea of freedom is a state of indecency. It's a state of obscenity. The English should be destroyed ...

The African tries to interrupt.

Now, sir, you're going to tell me that there's no colour bar in England . . . OFFICIALLY and that's all that matters . . . OFFICIALLY. You are FREE to go to that hotel over there in Park Lane ... OFFICIALLY. Every hotel which has a licence must take in travellers. The only trouble is that they see you travelling a bloody sight quicker than anyone else . . .

A man pushes his way to the front, and stares up at Ogilvie.

What are you doing up there?

I'm up here talking, says Ogilvie, and if you'll provide me with some clue as to what it is I should be talking about, so that it makes sense to you, I'll tell you why I'm up here talking. The notice on the front here says ROBERT OGILVIE, and that's to let ME know who I am.

Ogilvie? Lomas says, I haven't seen him for a long time. Is he in the park? he doesn't really belong there. Like Dr. Soper, you see, he could sell his form of articulacy elsewhere, to the radio or the newspapers. He knows that, and that's why he has no interest in the park. He has insulated himself from the implications of speaking in the park by his bitterness, a built in protective mechanism, like a nun with an oral contraceptive sewn in her cheek. There is no real fight left in the park, nothing to fight about, that's why I can only listen to the lunatics.

What about the anti-bomb people? says Freddie Kilennen.

Paring their nails with splinters from Nagasaki, Lomas says. That was short lived and it had nothing to do with the park. The lunatics in the park, the lunatic fringe is more intriguing. I tend to think that now. The crowd dismisses them immediately, whereas they pay attention to the politicians and the religious, because they're the tradition. I ask you, Freddie, I ask you, Cafferty, what political speakers have we left? the communists say they had the workers of the world behind them and it's made them intellectual hunchbacks. Bonar's gone, Jenner's gone and Conrad's gone now. Where are the religious speakers? Fred Law has left the park . . . but, the lunatics are intriguing. I regard what they're doing as a series of quiet cultural experiments. The political speakers are employing a psychology that we used up in the second world war.

You're right dear, says Freddie Kilennen, its a miserable bloody place.

*   *   *   *   *

The light has faded in the park, the tourists are pared away and the Salvation Army sings a final hymn before they close down until the late-night meeting:

> Tell me the old, old story
> Of unseen things above.
> Of Jesus and His Glory
> Of Jesus and His love.
> Tell me the story slowly
> That I may take it in . . .

Harry is over in Lyons with his friend Phil, and a woman in a leopard skin coat who is offering to pay his fine if he is summoned:

When I got out of that park, Harry is saying, that Police Inspector . . . he stabbed me under the ribs with his finger and he said that the park was a speaking area, and wasn't demarcated for performances or any other kind of ances. They called me over to their litter box and told me that I was a lunatic, and all that, and then they said that I'd had enough warnings and if I went on with it, they'd lock me up. I was getting too hot for them to handle.

He looks at the woman in the leopard skin coat.

I'm a bit of an Emeritus, you see, Harry goes on. I'm a philosopher. I'm a doctor, a pox doctor or any kind of doctor. I won't be the first one to have the first dose and you probably won't be the last. I had one dose and that was enough for me. So, you get your dose, and I tell you it's the overdose that does it. They've got nothing at the Palladium like me, and I'm seventy six. What's it matter? you see, for the last two and a half months I've been dealing with bits and pieces and odds and ends in the rag bag, but that one I was on about: As I see it . . . that one, you can apply that to yourself. It's rather humorous and it's only just come into my metaphors . . . AS I SEE IT.

*   *   *   *   *

In the park a white friar takes over from a brown one on the Catholic Evidence Guild platform and he says that he is not opposed to corporal punishment in certain circumstances, and Lil says that he is a fascist pig.

It is now dark. Norman takes up a stand by the railings under the hissing gaslamp. He stands on one leg, with his hands out-stretched, bares his teeth and moves up and down. Then he places the other leg on the ground and moves up and down. When a few people walk away from the fringes of other meetings and stand round him, he begins to speak, accompanying each phrase with a movement. His whole body reaches for the words; they are delivered very slowly:

You will . . . OBSERVE . . . if you are not . . . READING . . . that when you throw . . . that when you throw a . . . STONE on the water . . . and it . . . and it . . . it RIPPLES, and the RIPPLES . . . get more . . . get more . . . get, get PROGRESSIVELY . . . bigger . . . and bigger . . . and they . . . they . . . EMANATE . . . outwards to the edge of the pond, SO . . . SO . . .

Careful, says the richly dressed Irishman, careful. You'll grind the gears.

Norman ignores him: SO . . . some people find these ripples . . . find these ripples . . . a disTURBing feature . . . in their . . . in their . . . in their STONE throwing activity. EVEN, you see . . . EVEN by a form of tech . . . of tech . . . of TECHNOLO-GICAL PROGRESS . . . no one has ever found a method of throwing a stone into the pond . . . into the pond . . . without it . . . without it . . . without it . . .

Causing a ripple, says the richly dressed Irishman.

. . . without it . . . without it . . . CAUSING a ripple. And, do you
know? . . . do you know? I sometimes . . . sometimes WONDER,
who will HIT upon it first: the Russians or the Americans . . . I
want there to be no . . . no . . . no BACKLOG. Keep ALIVE
throwing a stone into a pond, or . . . or . . . or . . . or the IDEA
of throwing a stone into a pond. I mean, I mean, I want this . . .
this . . . this WORLD to say that the British no longer lead the
world as they used to . . . no longer lead the world as they used to
. . . but they . . . but they . . . they DO DO THIS.

Norman moves onto his right leg and raises the left one.

You see . . . I do this every Sunday night . . . that is BEFORE
. . . BEFORE I go to . . . go to . . . go to bed, and just after,
just . . . after the after . . . just after the afternoon has . . . has . . .
has HAD it. And I ask myself the question . . . where? I say . . .
where would this country be today, if it wasn't where it is now?
We'd be out in the middle of the . . . out in the middle of the . . .
out in the middle of whatever it is we're only to one side of now . . .

You're a very good dancer, says the richly dressed Irishman.
Norman slowly moves into another position which will help his
delivery.

I wish, Norman says, I wish that I was as good a . . . as good a
. . . as good a DANCER . . . as . . . as you are a bad LISTENER.
I mean, I come HERE . . . I spend . . . I spend . . . I spend WEEKS
AND WEEKS AND WEEKS of HARD earned study . . .
learning my lecture . . . learning my lecture by HEART . . .
GETTING my facts . . . getting my facts . . . getting other
people's facts . . . and then mixing them all up and coming here
and giving you the benefit of my . . . benefit of my . . . benefit of
my . . . benefit of my SAGACITY.

The Irishman mutters something. Norman overhears. He walks
across to him and drops his gymnastic form of speech:

Do you want to run this meeting? you can if you wish, you
know, you can have all these people, you can carry on and see
what a success you make of it.

The man walks away. Norman strains his body into another questing position:

This is the . . . this is the . . . this is the SHAPE. The shape is IMPORTANT, and not only the . . . not only the . . . not only the SHAPE . . . but also the . . . also the . . . also the COLOUR, of whatever it is I'm speaking about, which is part and parcel of . . . sometimes not just part and parcel . . . but often . . . often THE WHOLE THING and part and parcel . . .

What is the subject? Cafferty says.

I've nearly . . . I've nearly . . . I've nearly EXHAUSTED the subject.

Are you a philosopher? Cafferty says.

No . . . I'm a perfectly ordinary kind of man . . . I come up here . . . come UP here, and . . . and I see there's a need for people to be talked at. People want somebody to . . . to . . . to RAM HOME AT THEM . . . It could be some religious . . . some religious . . . religious TRIPE.

He raises both hands in the air above his head.

IT ALL BOILS DOWN TO THE FACT THAT WE SPEAKERS ARE THE . . . ARE THE . . . WE ARE THE . . .

He folds his hands behind his back, looks down at the ground:

When you take off . . . whatever it is that you've . . . you've GOT ON, you're going to feel cold . . . and on a . . . on a . . . on a HOT day, you're going to feel . . . going to feel . . . going to feel JUST THAT LITTLE BIT COOLER . . .

What are you doing? Cafferty says.

I'm trying to be an interesting public speaker. What are you trying to do by listening to me?

But what exactly are you doing? Cafferty says.

Well, I'm MAD. What's your excuse for coming here? It is my proud boast that you learn as much from me as you learn from anyone else in Hyde Park. You go away from me . . . go away from me . . . knowing that if you can't . . . if you can't

. . . that nobody else CAN . . . and then we're all in the same . . . all in the same . . .

BOAT, says the richly dressed Irishman, who has returned and pushed his way to the front.

All in the same . . .

BOAT.

All in the same . . . no, it doesn't matter, because we're all in it. And if, one day, when we hope we . . . when we hope we're all in, I would say that makes the . . . that MAKES the . . . But I'm going to go round that, and push on . . . push on.

If you look at it very closely . . . under a beer glass you will find . . . if you find it . . . and you have not previously . . . previously . . . previously LOST it . . . make sure that you DON'T LOSE IT AGAIN. And the best place . . . the best place . . . best place to keep one is under a . . . under a . . . under a MACHINE . . . IN under the machine. The base of the machine is made of . . . made of . . . made of a PECULIAR kind of . . . PECULIAR kind of soft wood which melts in gaslight. I will come to the eye of the . . . eye of the . . . eye of the . . . in a minute. DON'T NOBODY . . . NOBODY JUMP THE GUN.

He puts the leg he has been slowly moving in the air back on the ground and takes off his green beret.

I'm going to have a little break now, Norman says, because I feel I'm getting hemmed in and I want to let my remarks soak in . . . SOAK IN . . . and become part of you. I'm going to close the meeting, have a break, wander round, get some ideas that you haven't heard before . . . before you hear them, if you ever do. I may not speak, I may only move about, but whatever I do, you'll know that it's me doing it. I want to dry out for a minute or two, dry out and warm my hands . . .

Norman goes to the electric hand dryer in the Marble Arch lavatories, presses the pedal and moves his numbed hands in the air stream; his fingers tremble like stick insects. Then he goes through the turnstile to the lavatories, makes a note for his next meeting of the rubric inserted between the situations vacant columns on the lavatory walls: only a wit comes here to shit.

Why does he speak in that style? Cafferty says.

He repeats himself, says Lomas. He has repeated himself enough to have made an exact replica of himself before the final countdown.

*   *   *   *   *

The National Secular Society meeting is ending. The crowd and the speaker move off to another meeting above a public house in Seymour Street.

They only go to all those meetings afterwards to save heat, save on the gas meter, says Freddie Kilennen. Ask them what the meeting was about and they just tell you that it was warm in there.

The Salvation Army's late-night meeting is closing down. The rolls of canvas with the hymns painted on are strapped up and the flag is furled. But the Salvationists are ordered to mingle with the crowds of other speakers before they go home, to do some field work.

Tell me, says the major, tell, me, where do you live?

What's it matter? says Cafferty.

I'm asking you, my brother, where you live because when I saw you last week with our other brother, I forget his name. . . .

Lomas, Cafferty says.

Ah yes, when I saw you last week with our brother Lomas, who also says that he doesn't believe in God, I thought that I'd seen you somewhere before.

Oh.

Yes, says the major, yes, you used to live in Lisson Street, didn't you? I've seen your face there.

I lived there for a bit in June, says Cafferty.

That's right, says the major, that's right. I knew I was right. You go round associating with our brother Lomas who is an atheist, and you hold such views yourself, and yet my brother, and yet you are prepared to accept our Lord's hospitality in Lisson Street Salvation Army hostel. Do you not think it curious?

The police change their shift. The new lot come into the park with torches hanging by a strap to the button of their breast pockets. They use them to spot indecent behaviour in the crowds which have drawn closer together.

The queers arrive from the trade bars in the west end, looking for rent. They filter into the crowd under the trees. The queers known as Caligula and Mary Pickford watch the police:

When I see law in the crowd, says Caligula to Freddie Kilennen, right close to me when I'm working and I haven't noticed, I can FEEL, I can actually FEEL the chemistry of my body changing.

Mary Pickford turns to watch a new addition to the trade which works the park after the bars close. He is walking from group to group with a white raincoat draped over his shoulders.

Pick a grain out of that dish, dear, says Mary Pickford. You can tell she's been at the flour bags.

If I had a turkey like that, I wouldn't stuff it, says Caligula. Trolling round the park as if she owns it. Who is she, anyway?

He takes out a packet of cigarettes, slides two out with the long filters neck and neck.

Did you see Nutty Des got knocked off down in Clapham? tablets, dear . . . tablets. She used to carry them in a polythene bag, ate them like dolly mixtures . . .

The Irish political speaker is closing down his meeting:

. . . and was harnessed to the cause of imperialism with the support of Doctor Lucy's Catholic and Protestant bishops, the Protestant industrialists and landlords throwing dust in the face of Ireland. To hell with the lot of them, North and South, Catholic and Protestant bishops, Catholic and Protestant opulents. We are

not concerned with their opinions and interests, we are concerned
with the opinions and interests of the mass of the workers who
have suffered at their hands. Our party is the first step. Thank
you very much . . .

Do you finish up by singing the Red Flag? says a man who
knows several versions of it.

No, says the speaker. He announces the place and time of a
meeting commemorating the annniversary of the death of Wolfe
Tone, and gets down.

Have you any sympathy for the Irish cause? Cafferty says,
finding Lomas in the crowd.

A little, Lomas says.

Why was it that no one took that speaker seriously?

I think this is the reason, Lomas says, why none of the speakers
are taken seriously. When people come into the park, they just
think of it as an industry of insanity for the benefit of the tourists,
which is how I, in my old age, prefer to think of it. But that is a
constricting convention. When a man speaks in this park and he
has a serious message, which is rare, they don't take him seriously,
not because he doesn't represent anyone, but because, on account
of that convention, which is partly their fault, he's prevented
from representing himself.

The man with the silent message spots them. He gets off the
milk crate on which he has been standing all day in silence, with
his newspaper folded under his arm, and joins them.

I see the matter this way, Mr. Lomas, he says, if you don't mind
my interrupting for a brief spell. I think that I am the only speaker
in this park who doesn't come here to solve the world's problems
in one way or another. I see the matter this way: there would be
chaos if I were to add myself to their number, and this chaos
would arise from the problem solvers of the world eventually
being thrown onto the labour market. This would propagate
chaos, because they're suitable for nothing else than solving

problems, and I would be involved in it. I should also like to
mention another thing. If I produced a fact and distributed it to
my audience while I was on the platform, I should be picketed by
the Encyclopaedia as a blackleg.

But you don't say anything, says Lomas.

No.

What's the most revealing thing that anyone's ever said to you
while you've been stuck up on that platform saying nothing? says
Cafferty.

I don't know . . . I think . . . there have been things, I would say
that, yes there have been things, but I'm too bound up in my own
terminologies and other thoughts to notice them very much.

Freddie Kilennen has been discussing birth control with Mr.
Pearson, but he tires of his high pitched voice and exaggerated
accent and leaves with Caligula and Mary Pickford for another
meeting.

Goodbye, says Mr. Pearson, and turns round looking at the
small crowd which has collected. After smoothing back his hair
at the temples with his hands, he begins again.

Well, it seems that I've got people to listen to our discussion. I
may mention that I come here on Sunday nights to talk about this
subject and to try and recommend people to READ . . . there is a
book, you see, which would convince ANY unbiased person that
this population explosion is the centre of ALL our problems, and
unless we help people in underdeveloped countries one hundred
per cent, we'll get our atom war . . . As I see it, the bomb
is nature's method of redressing the balance. AT EVERY
MOMENT a new unfeedable child is born in India, increases the
destitution and then India may explode in chaos. At any moment
the East West barbarians will step in and you get your atom war
. . . it's the URGENCY of the problem . . . it's the ROOT of the
problem . . . we MUST try and enlighten the people. Now it's
been worked out that in four hundred years' time, there'll be one

person per square yard. This HYSTERICAL IMBALANCE . . .

A man steps forward, shaking a bottle with his thumb over the mouth of it. A yellow foam swells up inside.

Who are you talking there? and who are you to talk?

There are LARGE bodies of prejudicial doctrine at work, Mr. Pearson goes on, speaking faster and faster and heightening the tone of his voice. LARGE bodies of prejudicial doctrine . . . like the communists. The communists, you see, WANT destitution in the underdeveloped countries . . . and AMERICA, you see, THEY won't teach contraception in the East, you see, they'll lose the catholic vote . . .

The man releases his thumb from the mouth of the bottle. The liquid squirts over Mr. Pearson. He walks away, picks up a copy of the London Letter from Alfred Reynolds who duplicates it and distributes it in the park, and reads the quotation from Goethe on the front with satisfaction as he leaves:

ERROR IS CONTINUALLY REPEATED IN ACTION. THAT IS WHY WE MUST CONTINUALLY REPEAT THE TRUTH IN WORDS.

English to the core, says Lomas, which he has always been trained to eat. He extends his anxiety patterns and he calls it progress.

Why does he come up here? Cafferty says.

I don't know.

People are always talking about: on the one hand, and on the other hand, before I find that they've exhausted either hand, says the man with the silent message.

*   *   *   *   *

The few that are left wander round and round the tarmac, renewing their licence for saying the same things over and over again.

Harry comes across the tarmac without his Paternoster, and

wanders down one of the paths leading to the lake. He stops
beneath a gas-light, bends down, lays his hat on the ground,
leans his head into the middle of it, and raises his legs. As he stands
on his head his trousers ruck up round the knees and his bald
legs shine leprous in the light.

This shows that I'm too hot for them to handle, he says lower-
ing his legs. They can't stop me. No man has got the answer to
any of the world's problems. Ten thousand Churchills, Cham-
berlains, Stalins . . . with all their intelligence, it wouldn't fill a
grain of sand. They say I'm mad as a cut snake, that's because I'm
getting too hot for them to handle.

A mood that tends to fail, Lomas says; and Harry picks up his
hat and takes a path leading out of the park to Bayswater.

The police watch Mary Pickford underline his eyes with
cigarette ash, and take him off for winking at a man in the crowd.

It is five to twelve. The police move across the tarmac, herding
the small groups of people to the gates. They refuse to answer
questions about Mary Pickford and move slowly and silently,
with enough repressions to win a world war.

Come on, says Lomas, they want us to go.

The man with the silent message picks up his milk crate and
pushes it far under the refreshment stall with his umbrella. The
park empties. An old bum known as Richard is turned off the
subway steps by the lavatories where he is trying to sleep. He
crosses the Edgware Road and buys some potato salad at the
Marble Arch Barbecue. He walks on up the road with the lining
of his overcoat slashed and tied in a knot which swings against his
knees.

Van Dyn, Webster and Axel have left hours ago. MacGuinness
has spent the money he collected in the park on drugs, and stands
in the alleyway behind the *New Inn*, his body screwed up, his face
mangling itself like a dying fish.

Richard stares at him.

This is the end of the Manorial System, he says and walks on.

Lomas and Cafferty overtake on their way back to Kilburn with Freddie Kilennen who picked up some tablets from the queers and is saying that he is God.

Nietzsche killed God, Lomas says.

Ah, shut your face.

*   *   *   *   *

The police leave. The litter bins are full. A fog wreathes over the tarmac. The park gates are bolted.

I am NOT paranoiac. Everyone IS looking at me. Everyone IS following me.

MacGuinness

HE IS unshaven, ragged, stained and toothless, which leaves him with no control of his lips. They are like the eyelids of a man with his eyes put out.

He wears part of a Glenurquhart tweed suit, and in summer a large colonial style grey jacket, either flecked or filthy. The hair is black and parted if there is enough of it: sometimes it is short, sometimes it is long and rancid. He wears a gold ear-ring in the left ear, or a safety pin hooked into it, if the ring is in the pawn. He is five foot two.

He talks almost all the time, but his speaking from a platform always coincides with the end of the National Assistance money collected the week before from Praed Street in a taxi. He put whatever insurance stamps he ever had on a letter.

People come up to MacGuinness time and time again at the refreshment stall in the park asking him to speak, but he refuses. He's the only speaker who walks away from a crowd, but if he wants money from them, nothing will stop him. He can beg the milk from their tea.

MacGuinness then in Hyde Park: He stands on an oil drum, hunched up and twisting round like a snake on a stick, speaking in every direction; his tongue is dry as a parrot's, and he sticks it out for punctuation. It doesn't have much other use, covered as it is with white moss and tongue scab. The talking goes on at the back of his throat, the harsh Irish vowels wound out by an athletic epiglottis.

Now when you go into a toilet in this country, says Mac-Guinness to the crowd, all you can see is the writing on the wall, and it doesn't mean Kilroy was here. Every lavatory cleaner in England is a frustrated journalist. Who else could be responsible? The average time spent in a lavatory by members of the British public is six point seven minutes, which does not give them enough time to transfer all the rabid mutterings of their fertile minds. . . .

He starts speaking over his shoulder and spots a woman in the crowd behind him. He turns round to face her:

Have we been married?

She laughs; makes no reply.

No brain . . . no brain at all. Nothing upstairs . . . but have you seen the staircase? Now we live in an age of falsies lass, and in this age of falsies, you will always find that a woman with a big bust has a small brain and a woman with a small bust, Jesus she's no brain at all.

Now I came over here to make my second million pound. . . .

He spots another woman in the crowd, turns round to face her and goes on slowly:

I think you've got what it takes. I don't know how long it is since you had it or who took it, but you've certainly got it. Have you got it with you? You left it in the bottom drawer for the wedding.

The woman leaves. MacGuinness talks faster:

Now in England today, as I have said, any man who is not queer is not normal. Any man who marries a woman is queer. Mixed marriages never . . . Now Christine Keeler as one of MacGuinness's ex-mysteries has done more damage to the British government than the Labour Party, the Mau Mau or the I.R.A. have done in the past forty bloody years. In that three months Christine Keeler made three hundred and fifty thousand pounds, she has a yacht, three houses, a pent house in Chelsea, two cars and a Jaguar. Will you ever get an income like that or a Jaguar working on the typer? Prostitution has not been and NEVER WILL BE a crime. Christine Keeler is a MODEL, like MacGuinness. Anyone can come up to my caravan and I'll pose for you any night of the week. I've got nothing to hide: I'm all man downstairs and all woman upstairs. You see, half the women in Soho are men and half the men in Soho are women. Once you realize that you're half way there.

Now I remember when I came over here first . . . well dressed, clean and very highly sexed. . . . I was walking down Greek Street, a notorious street for whores. This was the red lamp district and I was the light . . . and I was walking down this street straight over from Ireland.

This girl comes up. She glides across the street in my direction, and I hitched my eyes on to her . . . don't get excited at that . . . and there's a look of seduction in her eyes. She glides across the street and she skids to a halt. She says to me: Hello Paddy . . . well, I mean, my name is Bill. Why, hello miss, says I. Would you like to come home with me tonight? she says. Now at that time I was young. I was well fed, well dressed and very highly sexed. So, believing in the philosophy of Culchimok (if you don't take a step, you'll never break your neck), a great Irish philosopher, I took the ball on the hop and went home with this prostitute.

She was living in a very select flat. In the corner of the bedroom she has a smashing double bed, and on the bed was the first interior sprung mattress that I have ever seen. We jump into the bed. The next morning . . . after a sleepless night, she gets up, and I get up behind her. . . . I didn't mean it like that . . . and she makes me a lovely breakfast: bacon, eggs, sausages, tomatoes, spam . . . and as I was going out the door, she says to me in her very sexy voice: Paddy, she says, Paddy . . . what about the money? Ah well, miss, says I. Seeing you've been that nice to me and that kind to me, honest to Jesus I wouldn't dream of taking a penny off you.

Now a hundred years ago, you English, the few of you that are left, you were the most dynamic people the world has ever known. I mean· when you were out in the colonies and you were robbing and ravishing, you were men after my own heart. I couldn't wait to get over there to do some ravishing myself. And then eventually I arrived to find myself in London, having been led to believe that the streets were paved with gold. I walked from Piccadilly to Waterloo dirtying my fingers picking up Gold Flake dog ends. . . .

Well, many of you people in the audience must believe in the hereafter, I believe in it. I'm here after a few shillings. MacGuinness is the last of the free lance orators. MacGuinness earns his living by breaking the law. It is against the law for me to ask you for money, but its not against the law for you to give it me, which is of course the same thing. Those of you who wish to contribute to my upkeep: I assure each and every one of you that I shall not insult any one of you by refusing to take money off you. If you have no money, but you would give it me if you had it, there's no need to walk away. . . . SMILE . . . SMILE . . . don't let there be too many smiles though. Then again if you have money and you're enjoying listening to me, and you give me nothing, let me give you a bit of gypsy advice. When you get to a road: look left, look right and look left again, because if you were run down by a bus, honest to God I should hate to see you die with anything that belonged to me in your pocket.

He gets down from the platform, whips round the crowd with his hand out, and shovels the money into his side pocket. The last man he comes to just stares at him:

Come on, says MacGuinness, pay your fare.

You are Raftery the Poet playing to empty pockets, says the man.

I am not a poet, says MacGuinness, I'm a con man. Pay your fare.

The man pays.

He used to be such a great speaker, said Freddie Kilennen once to Lomas when they had been listening to MacGuinness in the park. Do you remember him before he took to the drugs?

Yes, said Lomas. He's still up to the standard. He has a very saleable personality . . . and he uses it for nothing, except money. If you have a saleable personality and you use it to make the breath of this or that -ism smell sweeter, your personality's in the wrong hands. But MacGuinness, he just slips his personality into the mind of the crowd and then they exorcize it by paying him. There are no side effects. He's just a tourists' Irishman . . . bleeding at the gills . . .

It takes some time for the platform manner to wear off. MacGuinness has to wait for some incident to occur before he tires of stopping people in the streets round Marble Arch, and asking them: How's your wife and my two babies getting on? and before one of the chains which link all the jokes is broken.

Either he is arrested, drugged, taken in hand by Betty Dracup, who has looked after him on and off for five years, or he is rebuffed; he once asked the newsvendor at Tottenham Court Road how his wife and MacGuinness's two babies were getting on. The newsvendor replied. MacGuinness took a newspaper from the newstand, gave the man two shillings, told him to keep the change and tore the paper into shreds, hurling them vainly at a poster for the film *Cleopatra*. KEEP THE CHANGE AND KEEP YOUR FILTHY PAPER. . . . The newsvendor replied again. The jokes were thwarted for a time.

MacGuinness belongs to the all night, under the armpit cafés in Cable Street and Monmouth Street; to the dosshouses, spikes and reception centres, in the sense that these are the places he frequents. But his vampire egoism and the drugs cushion him, against them:

Why MacGuinness this, MacGuinness that? said MacGuinness once in the *New Inn* when Cafferty had asked him why he was so full of himself. Why MacGuinness, MacGuinness all the time? because MacGuinness is every one. MacGuinness is you and Ray. Ray and me are brothers and you are Jesus Christ. Therefore I am the son of God. If you are schizophrenic, you are only half way there: God is a threesome . . .

MacGuinness got up to go to the bar.

He means, said Lomas, that his speech rhythms linger in the mind of the crowd. He's wrong.

Ray is the only person that MacGuinness seems to have any respect for. He used to live in the hutment in the middle of Soho Square in the war and kept a sleeping roll there. He planted Indian Hemp in the flower beds.

I swear, said MacGuinness coming back, that the grass growing there now is the pure blade of twilight.

But no one has ever seen Ray. MacGuinness left.

His egoism has to be justified by success, said Lomas when he had gone. In the end he's just a Hyde Park lunatic.

It is justified by success, said Freddie Kilennen. He had some articles in the *Irish Digest*.

I'll believe them when I see them, said Lomas.

The next week Freddie Kilennen brought them into the *New Inn*.

There are three of them, he said.

Read them out then, said Lomas. Read them out.

They're called *Smokes Are Where I Find Them*, said Freddie Killennen, *How to Fail At An Interview*, and *Ringsend Was Out On Its Own*. I'll read you the best bits. *Smokes Are Where I Find*

Them is about picking up butt ends. This is it: 'In the nick I've smoked . . .'

He's never been in the nick, said Lomas. All he's ever done is one day instead of the fine, on the Monday morning drunk and disorderly stint at Bow Street. . . .

Have a bit of patience, will you? this is fiction. 'In the nick I've smoked the fibre dust from my prison mattress. During the war I've smoked dried tea leaves and I once attempted to smoke turf. But how low can a man stoop? To the gutter! But to pick up dog-ends on a busy street without people knowing what you are doing is one of the lesser known arts. The man with the bowler hat would say, "I'd starve first." To this I would say, "You are not a real smoker sir." '

'No matter how high in life you are at the moment, it's only your wage package and your pride that keep you from the gutter. And it's so easy to get there. I was born in one; since then I've descended and arose from many, and I know that with a few bad breaks I may tomorrow in the coldness of an English dawn drone down London's Oxford Street on a wing and a prayer and divebomb for, perhaps, your castaway dog-end, sir. Or you for mine.'

Very witty, said Lomas.

Do you not think so? said Freddie Kilennen. It's from the *Irish Digest*, which is thought very highly of in some quarters, Here, this is what it says on the front: 'The *Irish Digest* brings you every month a concise and vivid cross section of Irish thought and life' . . . this one here, with the photograph of the hunt on the front. 'A crisp spring morning,' it says, 'eager thoroughbred hunters and staghounds . . . the members of the Ward Union Hunt are assured of all the thrills of the chase. But there is no kill. The cornered stag is retrieved and brought back to its comfortable quarters, where it lives to run another day.' . . . Photograph by Fogra Failte . . .

What's the other one? said Lomas.

How To Fail At An interview, said Freddie Kilennen.

Read it out then.

'How To Fail At An Interview' . . . it starts off: 'To do nothing and to do it slowly has long been the aim of my life,' and it provides a solution to the problem, 'when some civil servant of a hatch clerk, who takes his illness seriously or wishes to save the taxpayer's money by getting you a job, may try to inject you with his miseries by handing you a green card to go for an interview.' MacGuinness solves the problem by being dynamic during the interview, it is very witty, and he ends it up: 'Work is just another of Man's diseases and prevention is better than cure. If you don't look for work, it won't look for you. No man is born with the urge to work, for you cannot work and think.'

Is the next one called *Ringsend Was Out On Its Own*? said Lomas. Because the story goes that he was born there . . . used to work in a mattress factory, and he married there, he has a daughter in Galway they say. His wife died of galloping thrombosis and he never looked after her. The story goes that he went back to Ringsend when he'd saved up some money from the park (that's the suspicious part of it), and they stoned him out of the place. Read on.

Well I don't know about that, said Freddie Kilennen. But this is it: 'Many of the old landmarks had vanished the last time I was home, and some of the people I knew had been laid to rest. The old Ringsend clan are scattered to the four corners of the earth. Others have been housed in the new schemes in Ballyfermont and West Cabra. Though some remain, with all the people who moved in when the corporation built block after block of new flats, if I went home today I might be mistaken for a stranger. . . .'

MacGuinness came into the *New Inn*, and heard Freddie Kilennen reading his articles. Lomas looked away and pretended not to have been listening to them.

Where the hell did you get hold of those, Freddie?

Had them for a long time, dear.

Another MacGuinnessite. They're everywhere. But those articles are rubbish. My speeches are rubbish. I speak rubbish to the audience, but when I speak to myself I'm speaking to the intellectual few.

He bought a round of drinks three deep and left.

It seems that MacGuinness has the strongest connections with Ireland: his appearance, his accent, his manner and his past. A cousin of his, a Whelan, was hanged in Mountjoy in the civil war. But it's now only a device. He hardly ever mentions the place, and if he does it's only for commercial reasons. A man was once asking him some questions at the end of a meeting. These people are called come-ons, or punters, by the professional speakers, because they can be done for more money:

PUNTER: Why do you speak in Hyde Park?

MACGUINNESS: Last year I sent the old woman to Blackpool and she came back with her tongue sunburnt. I can't get a word in edgeways in my own home. The only answer to my frustrations is to get up on a soapbox and prove to myself that the Irish race is not a corpse.

PUNTER: But why do you speak there EVERY Sunday?

MACGUINNESS: I need the money. I'm the last of the lachikoes . . . a lachikoe is not a bohemian. A bohemian is a person who works to live but does not live to work. A bohemian is an imitation beatnik. A hundred per cent beatnik is only an imitation gypsy. I'm the king of the lachikoes, the king of the gypsies. I'm what every man is trying to be. With these two hands I have fought my way into the gutter.

PUNTER: Why did you come to England?

MACGUINNESS: I came to England at the expense of the Irish Republican Army in Dublin, and I was thrown out of the I.R.A. for being a rebel. Now that may sound paradoxical. How can you be a rebel in the midst of a rebel organization? I was asked

to blow up Charing Cross Station. I laid the mine . . . the Englishmen call it a screw, and I knew that if I didn't lay her some limey
would and the mine didn't go off till Tuesday.

PUNTER: What was the date?

MACGUINNESS: I came to England in . . . I don't know what
time it was. But at that time the jerry was knocking them down
and paddy was building them up. I came over here in 1984 to
take over from George Orwell, who was also a beatnik and a
tramp, only I made the big time while he was dead.

PUNTER: What did your father do?

MACGUINNESS: My father put de Valera into power and
never heard of him from 1915 to 1942, so it's possible to forge
a name in history.

PUNTER: Why do you call yourself the king of the gypsies?

MACGUINNESS: I'm not really a king. I'm only a shithouse
king. Pay your fare.

The man paid him about a farthing a word.

MacGuinness once said, said Lomas, that he has released
himself for ever from the burden of being Irish, by going up to
the commissionaire at the Cumberland Hotel and saying that his
grandmother Mary Ellen Brown, was the last person in Ireland
to be burnt at the stake for being a witch, and that history records
. . . the local papers of the time, that is . . . that when her mind
left her body, a cat appeared in the sky shouting I'LL BE BACK.
. . . I'LL BE BACK. The commissionaire said that he didn't
believe in witchcraft.

MacGuinness gave him ten shillings . . .

                *   *   *   *   *

MacGuinness gets high on sex, MacGuinness was saying.
MacGuinness gets high on hunger. MacGuinness gets high on
rich food. MacGuinness gets high on purple hearts. MacGuinness

gets high on aspros and coca cola. MacGuinness gets high on coal gas and milk. MacGuinness gets high on hemp and hashish. MacGuinness gets high on the ash of joss sticks mixed with tea and salt. MacGuinness gets high when he passes through Soho and smells the wet fish. . . . Every girl in Soho smells of wet fish . . .

The scene was Lisson Street Salvation Army hostel. A man from Kerry with a complicated quiff that shone some morning, had just taken some money off him on the strength of a prescription for purple hearts (amphetomene), with which he never returned.

The atmosphere had something to do with post-revolutionary ennui: the foetid coloured walls dictating the foetid smell, or the other way round. False gods trying to absolve themselves from nothing in particular. Bacilli dying behind the insurance stamps. The advertisement: SOMEONE, SOMEWHERE WANTS A LETTER FROM YOU.

He had a man with him: Stewart Menzies, whose brother was in prison for slashing a painting by Salvador Dali in Glasgow. I admire that, said MacGuinness. He admires me in the park, so I admire him on account of his brother.

They brought back trays of food from the canteen, and set them down at one of the tables. Some of the men there gathered round him.

Hello Mike, how's your wife and my two babies getting on?

Mike said that that only served to remind him of blank maintenance orders, but to carry on with the rubbish.

I'm glad you recognize the language I'm speaking, said MacGuinness. He changed the subject. Would you like to know what makes MacGuinness tick? would you like to know MacGuinness's philosophy?

The heads drew closer together.

I'll tell you my philosophy. . . . My grandmother was my mother, and that makes me my father's brother. But there are no women in heaven. God did not need a woman . . . a woman is a man made thing . . . now you understand homosexuality.

When your father's a man and your mother's a woman, you're half and half. When you make the two halves live in harmony, you're a man. Now I was in Warwick Avenue . . . Paddington Station . . . and there was this advertisement for the Co-Op, with a woman in it . . . she was TALKING to me. I was paralysed. The woman went out of me.

When a man is first born, he's a homosexual bisexual. You come out of a woman and you spend the rest of your life trying to get back inside. Every woman wants to have the first of her sons to see if she's made him well. Every man wants to take his daughter's virginity. And every girl wants to see what her father would be like as a lover . . . now you understand MacGuinness. We are all part of the same thing, and when they all fit together there's one part out of place, you think it's me. . . . I think it's you, or I think it's me and you think it's you. Mary and Joseph, they were in a position. The donkey was in a superior position. It had two speeds: very slow, and stop.

They looked very bored. Mike turned round to see if he could see the man MacGuinness gave the money to for the purple hearts:

Don't WORRY, said MacGuinness. Don't WORRY . . . don't you see? he won't come back. That's REAL metaphysics for you.

With long intervals of neglect, undernourishment and the lack of sleep induced by the barbiturates: amphetomene, drinamyl, and methedrine, his health always declines. He came up one night to a room that Cafferty had in Fashion St. E.1. He looked terrible. His beard had grown in patches on his face, as if he'd tried it with plantoids; his whole body trembled: became some sick joke about St. Vitus's dance. He had not eaten for days. His stomach was emaciated, and under a foul shirt his ribs clawed in and out at his lungs forcing them to breathe. He fidgeted. He stank. He was incontinent. He said that he was going to die. Cafferty believed him:

I am going to die . . . I used to say that I knew the exact date and place of my death, but I cheated fate by not being there . . . not carrying a watch. I don't say that now . . . I don't know. But I'm going to die. . . . It was terrible then, at the time of that joke, to know that I wasn't going to die after all. I am in your sub-conscious. I am in hundreds of thousands of subconsciouses. . . . I don't want followers. All the people I talk to in the street. I don't see them. They give you the bum stare, and you don't see them. You stare and stare at the sun and it burns up your atom . . . blinds you . . . blinds the atom in your eye . . . I used to have a spare atom . . . and with not much time to make sure I've been born first. I am going to die.

I want to tell you this: when anyone is going to take your mind, make it a blank. Stand in front of a high grey wall that you can't get over, and when you're flying high out of your mind, the smoke that you draw flows down, not up. Become the whorls of the smoke. . . . I am telling you this because at this moment I am the hand of fate, and I'm tired of it . . . tired of the loneliness. I'm cold . . . not that kind of coldness . . . you could drop in a heap in the street or the park, and they'd throw crumbs at you. When you've climbed three quarters of the way up the tree of evil knowledge, they nail you to it.

He said he was going to see Betty Dracup. Cafferty said he could sleep on the floor if he liked. He left. Two days later a letter arrived:

A BLOCK,
ST. FRANCIS HOSPITAL,
EAST DULWICH,
S.E.22

From the home of the Insane, I send you
GREETINGS
As Dawn broke yesterday Morning, I could have been (and I was) seen running Naked spear in hand through Regent's Park.

I would like you to come and See me here in this Gipsy Camp of

Higher Interlect. Every (NUT) here is a great guy. And they all Dig Your Daddy Like Crazy Man. They really dig me. Because in me they see themselves.

I have no Doubt, you will be glad to hear that I have found, what the Inner Council of Gipsies will recognize as my grandmother's long lost Broomstick. With this means of transportation all things are now possible. And the farest distances is now but a thought away. Dig me. Dig, my son.

> *I will see You when I see You.*
> *Here I will remain for a while*
> *Yours till a blade of grass*
> *become a tree.* I AM.
> *Billy the 1st, MacGuinness*
>   *King of Gipsies.*

The hospital lies at the end of a strand of a road off the bottom of Denmark Hill, with anti-therapeutics at every turn: instructions to ring bells, glass bulbs at the tops of pillars sign-written ST FRANCIS in scaled paint, instructions to curb noise in the form of Fougasse drawings of a tap dripping the word SILENCE in larger and larger letters; deep fingernail marks in the Government Property toilet rolls.

A woman in the visitors' waiting room closed her eyes every time Cafferty released a quantity of tobacco fumes from his throat. She spoke about the District Line of the railway underground:

With the District Line, trains come in EVERY THREE MINUTES, and if you miss one . . . then there's ALWAYS ANOTHER. YOU ONLY HAVE TO WAIT AN AVERAGE OF ONE AND A HALF MINUTES.

MacGuinness was in the Observation Ward. He was eating, but he stopped:

Hello . . . hello. I get four meals a day here, and get higher on waiting for them than I've been on anything . . .

When he was sufficiently high on waiting for the food, he went back to eat it. But the conversation was interrupted by a man hopping on one foot, who had translated diaries by a contemporary of Cellini, who ate goats' brains; or he ate them himself and was waiting to be released from the Observation Ward of the hospital to eat the other half of an unfinished goat's brain, unobserved. It was in Earls Court. Cafferty made a note.

To MacGuinness the place meant nothing. He had daubed a large notice in the Occupational Therapy Ward: MAC-GUINNESS SLEPT HERE AND LEFT WITHOUT PAYING HIS RENT, and in small biro letters at the foot: how else can one hope to remain in the memory of the commercial classes?

Above his bed he had written: All the great men are dead. Omar Khayyam is dead. Confucius is dead. Oscar Wilde is dead. I am not feeling too well myself.

His only worry was that he would be classed as a professional mental patient, and deprived of four meals a day to fall back on when he wanted them, once the initial requirements were fulfilled. The initial requirements have been fulfilled eight times. Once for trying to break into Buckingham Palace to ask for a glass of water: Lomas had spoken of the incident, saying that exhibitionism was suppressed more for shame at the reaction which it prompts than for anything else.

MacGuinness described the last time he was in the mental home:

I was arrested in Hyde Park at three o'clock in the morning. The police found me kneeling on my hands and knees eating grass . . . it was about three months ago. They gave me twenty eight days in Tooting Bec Mental Hospital. 'Grazing on the Queen's Highway without a licence.' You see, with all their intelligence they couldn't say to themselves: Now why was that man eating grass? If I saw a man eating grass, by Jesus I'd say that man was hungry. . . .

The only problem the hospital seemed to have was the recovery of MacGuinness's clothes. They wanted him out of the place as soon as possible, but MacGuinness was quite prepared to take off the peasant clothes provided by the hospital and walk out of it as he had been brought in originally by the meat waggon from Regent's Park. Cafferty asked him about the incident:

You know, son, said MacGuinness I found a little jungle in the middle of the park, Regent's Park, and I could have charged around in it with my spear, bollock naked, and nobody would have noticed. I buried all my writings there. But I decided to go out and face the widening dawn. So they nicked me.

The next day the police had found his clothes, and his writings: The Terrible Confessions of a Gipsy Vamp, and he was told that he would be released the next day. Betty Dracup came to see him. She is much older than MacGuinness; and when she could get about more, she used to keep a fruit barrow just outside the park gates. Before that she worked on the buses, and before that she was a stripper. She still has her hair dyed a flash blonde. The charge nurse showed her in, and she sat at a table with MacGuinness:

Did you bring me my favourite tonic wine? said MacGuinness, taking a bottle from his pocket. The stocks are running low.

I did not, said Betty. Put that away, put it away. I came down to see that you were all right and to let you know that there was nothing that I could do about your clothes. I'm going to have a rest . . . I'm going away out. It's not the house that's closing in on me, it's the people. . . . I didn't come down here to tell yous, I didn't come down to moan, but I'm going to have a rest: twenty one days voluntary patient as a mental drug addict. Not your kind of drugs.

You have a rest, said MacGuinness. I mean you might as well avail yourself of all the amenities of the welfare state.

I went to the doctor, this morning, Betty went on. I got the form . . . and these pills. The first day you feel all muscle, then . . . then the muscles of the chest start to loosen . . . then the muscles of the mind start to loosen . . . You couldn't care less . . . and if you've lived as I . . . when I used to worry: where's he going tomorrow, where will he go? But I'm getting away from the whole lot of yous . . .

Bad neighbours.

Not only bad neighbours, said Betty. Bad everything. Public Assistance . . . the council . . . the Labour Exchange is turning me pig sick. The people outside of me make me ashamed . . . put me up the pole. The whole Tom, Dick and Harry . . . and I want to get away from yous. You'd let me die as soon as look at me, like you did your wife. Your daughter in Galway might be dead for all you know . . . you've seen her twice in your life. The whole universe is knocking me pig sick. You've been in eight times, and who's got you out, every time? who stopped them from certifying yous? Betty Dracup . . . Betty Dracup. Well, this is the last time.

I'm sticking to purple hearts, said MacGuinness.

They're no good. These are eight and six on prescription and you walk on air, said Betty, taking a tube of pills from her handbag. They have this inside to keep the pills dry. Those purple hearts are cushioning. Goldie told me. I said to the doctor: just give me something to make me high. I'm so depressed I'm hitting the bottom. I could kill yous. I could kill everything. I'm in a terrible state.

Yes, said MacGuinness.

The charge nurse came over.

Well doctor, said Betty. What was wrong with him?

He was brought in by the police with no clothes on, said the charge nurse. Apparently he had been running round Regent's Park with no clothes on and a spear in his hand saying that he was the last of the Mohicans . . .

What was wrong with that? said Betty. Does that mean he's a psychopath?

Well, said the charge nurse, a sociopath.

What's that? said Betty, some kind of rebel?

He was also suffering from what they term arbitrary discharge from the speech centre, said the charge nurse.

He was vaccinated with a gramophone needle, said Betty.

The charge nurse turned to MacGuinness, and handed him a book:

Thinking that you were a catholic, Mr. Rees suggested that I give you this. It's a treasury of devotion . . .

On the outside, said MacGuinness, and its *Forever Amber* on the inside. Have you any swinging drugs?

Betty left. The charge nurse showed her out.

Look after her, said MacGuinness to Cafferty as he got up, look after her. She's ill . . . very, very ill. I'll be out in the morning. Are they queuing up for me in the park?

He comes up to the park the following Sunday, sees the man with feathers in his hair on a platform shouting: ANYBODY WANT TO WHIP ME FOR TWO POUND, takes off his belt and starts to whip him round the ankles. The man with feathers in his hair jumps off the platform and scurries away. A larger crowd gathers:

The other day, says MacGuinness, I went into a mental home. Now to be mad is one of the national characteristics of the Irish. The English expect it of them and Jesus, we never let them down. To the gypsy, or to the Apache Indian there is no such word as madness. Madness only means that the gods have taken the person's mind. And a man or woman must have a great mind when the gods have need of it, for the gods have everything. Madness is the highest form of intelligence, and combined with common sense, madness is pure genius. Now when I arrived. . . . Would you like to know why I went mad? I am a man who has nothing to hide. To prove it, last Sunday morning I ran stark naked through Regent's Park worshipping the golden rain and shouting that I was the last of the Mohicans. . . . SIR, YOU

MUST WEAR CLOTHES. Who says you must wear clothes? The tailor and cutter.

Take the example of a man walking barefooted. That's the only way a man stands on his own two feet. You try walking round barefooted. By Jesus, every single one you meet will offer you a pair of shoes. I had a friend once, his name was Teddy Gordon. He was an Irish Jamaican Arab. The Jewish Buddha. He used to FLOAT round London. No shoes. They say you must wear shoes. You must do this, you must do that. You push the English, that doesn't matter. You push the Americans, that doesn't matter. You push the blacks, that doesn't matter. But the day you push the gypsies, you'll blow yourself up. They're going nowhere.

Now when Prince Philip goes to visit a mental home, he lets everybody know he's going in. Any muck is covered up. When MacGuinness goes in, he goes in as a patient and nobody knows that MacGuinness is in till MacGuinness has gone. Now you must dig this national health, this Mental Health Act. The greatest drug addicts in this country are the doctors. Doctors are all drug addicts. Psychiatrists are waiting to use you as guinea pigs. Do you know that there are people in mental hospitals who've been in FOR THIRTY FIVE BLOODY YEARS FOR BREAKING A WINDOW IN THEIR OWN HOME? You've got to have someone to bail you out, and who's going to take responsibility for someone that society says is a lunatic?

Now MacGuinness IS a lunatic. MacGuinness is that mad that they won't have me in the mental home. I drive everybody sane. You don't see me getting up at six o'clock in the morning to go to work. You know what the nurses do now? They get up at a quarter to five and cycle eleven miles to give a lunatic a cup of tea. I RECOMMEND IT. . . . YOU'RE LIVING IN A MAD SOCIETY, SO GO MAD! and they put all these men and women together and by Jesus, if you can't get sex in a mental home, you can't get sex in a brothel. They're all going MAD with sex . . . so if you feel a bit run down . . . GO MAD!

Now every time I pray to God I find that I am talking to
myself. Let me tell you the difference between sanity and madness.
If you go round London talking to yourself, they'll certify you.
But you can go round London all day talking to your wife and
she's not listening, and you're normal.

Were you really in the madhouse? says a man coming up to
him after the meeting.

Yes, says MacGuinness. And I left my false teeth at number 8
Marshall Street, North Soho. It's been pulled down now . . .
turned into a car park. Pay your fare.

What was the madhouse like? said Lomas when Cafferty came
back to the *New Inn* after the meeting.

No different from any other place, said Cafferty. No different
from schools, police stations, houses of parliament, prisons . . .
normalcy on its uppers.

Lomas stared into his glass.

They all lie at the end of one grimy definition, he said. Why
did they put MacGuinness there?

Because he likes going there, said Freddie Kilennen.

But they don't KNOW that, said Lomas. They put you in the
madhouse under a twenty eight day observation order to test
your awareness of reality, only they call it a hospital to
suggest that some corner of reality has been captured for it,
and . . .

Ah, shut your face, he enjoyed the place, said Freddie Kilennen.
It's material for the park.

Lomas turned to Cafferty:

What did they say to him in there?

They said that if he went on with the drugs he'd overtax his
metabolism and his brain cells would burn out.

There you are you see, said Freddie Killennen. They were only
trying to help him.

They also said that they might put him on the black list of
professional patients.

And the same goes for that dear, said Freddie Kilennen. They were only trying to help him.

What did he do all the time he was in there? said Lomas.

He made Jokes, said Cafferty, but he did do a piece of writing: Dust to Dust. I have it somewhere . . .

Read it out, said Lomas getting up for the pub was closing. Read it out. Cafferty and Lomas left the *New Inn* and turned right down the alleyway. Freddie Kilennen came out a moment later, walked past them, and went home up the Edgware Road.

Good, said Lomas. Read it out.

Here it is, said Cafferty. He wrote it in the occupational therapy room:

Dust to dust by William MacGuinness.

The street of silent night re-echoed its longing for quietness. These people who live with death and know not life, but must one day die, before learning how to live. And a man kissed a girl and stopped because of me, who would not have stopped for him, and she smiled knowingly. And they passed on and were swallowed in the roar of one of the numberious midnight mad motor-bikes. And still the maddening roar denied my street the sleep it was due. And my longing for tea made me energetic and lent wings to my flattering feet. And the milk flowed slowly as if time was dragging the anchor of spaceless space in an attempt to put an end to all which has not yet begun. For I knew that I was all things and nothing. And nothing mattered any more. And as my nothingness became all things, the vibrations grew less and less frequent and the street began to doze in peaceful repose. For the day had been long and the footsteps many, for now I had become the street, and because I worried the worries of the street were transferred to me, who must now transfer them back from where they first came from you to you. For I, the street, a man made thing of dried up muck, am made of dust like you. And the street was made to uplift man while it remains down trodden. Then, if all things be made of dust, pray then who are you, to tell a man who is the street, what he must and must not do?

The last bit rhymes, said Cafferty when he had finished reading it.

Yes, said Lomas. Yes . . . interesting. . . . There is a secret MacGuinness that you don't see in the park.

There is, said Cafferty. Do you remember the time he had the Christ complex and made a pilgrimage to Liverpool with a cross on his back to ask the Liverpool police for a glass of water, and they locked him up for wandering abroad and vagrancy? He came back and said that they'd locked him up for seventy two hours, and that that was a symbolic period of time. That was the secret MacGuinness in action . . .

Perhaps, said Lomas. Perhaps . . . It's drugs that brings it out of him isn't it. I should like to see the secret MacGuinness in action, the bit beyond the jokes . . . I've known him for twenty years, and never really seen beyond the jokes . . .

The conversation grew more involved, but the death of it was that they parted company. Lomas went down to Shepherds Bush, and picked up a tape recorder. Cafferty picked up some tablets and some marijuana from nowhere in particular, and two bottles of surgical spirit from an all night chemist's. They met up at Cumberland Gate, went into the park and lured MacGuinness out of it. It was about a quarter to twelve at night. MacGuinness fancied the idea.

They went towards Charing Cross and ended up in the Victoria Embankment Gardens. MacGuinness had drunk most of the surgical spirit, and washed down half the tablets. He was silent, and sat down in front of a statue of a little girl holding out a bowl with two hands inscribed: FROM THE CHILDREN OF THE LOYAL TEMPERANCE LEGION IN MEMORY OF THE WORK DONE FOR THE TEMPERANCE CAUSE BY LADY HENRY SOMERSET, PRESIDENT OF THE NATIONAL BRITISH WOMAN'S TEMPERANCE ASSOCIATION. INCORPORATED JUNE 1896. 'I WAS THIRSTY AND YE GAVE ME DRINK.'

MacGuinness seemed to be in a trance. Lomas handed him the tape recorder:

Dictate the secret MacGuinness into that, said Lomas.

MacGuinness took the machine, laid it in the flower bed and held the microphone up to his face. He spoke into it, staring all the time at the statue of the little girl or to his far right, where there was a statue of John Stuart Mill. The pauses are evenly indicated, but sometimes were several minutes long:

In the beginning . . . before the beginning began . . . a way back before that, to when even space was only considered to be a madman's dream, and when there were those that thought I couldn't make it . . . I was born and reared in the valley of Tir Na Og . . . Eldorado . . . Shangri La . . . the land of everlasting youth . . .

Ringsend? said Lomas.

Leave me alone, said MacGuinness. Leave me alone to my thoughts.

Lomas and Cafferty went away to the benches further down the gardens, and slept.

MacGuinness went on dictating to the machine:

I was twenty . . . my father was twenty . . . No man ever aged a day after his twentieth year. I was in the sun . . . and flying high as kites . . . flying high in the sun . . . and I had one weakness . . . I wanted to light a cigarette . . . I burnt my . . . hand.

The brown leaf of the graveyard . . . myself, the doveabee . . . D-O-V-E-A-B-E-E . . . the daughter of the darkness . . . Mac-Guinness . . . M-A-C-G-U-I-N . . . double N . . . double N . . . strange looking men as the companions on the blank park benches, in what could be described as the early hours of the morning. Cars pass, to and fro from here and there, in a homeless trap. I lie back in the earth and try to sleep. It's no good.

The companions are staring at me, trying to uncover this mask . . . I am not paranoiac . . . everyone IS looking at me, everyone IS staring at me. This little girl is lost, she has strayed and is lost among the teeming millions of London, and the old man . . . wearing a hat and an old satchel, seated over there, full stop. He is old and badly dressed. His eyes are hookahs for the whole spectacle . . . better inform the police . . .

There comes a falling leaf . . . my cigarette goes out. It has gone out slowly, comma. Better inform the . . . better. . . . In gypsy circles, they smoke when the graveyard is being dug . . . the leaf of the graveyard. When the grave is dug, it is òut. . . .

The girl is a deaf mute . . . born in a land of solitude. She gets down . . . walks over to me . . . I cannot see. A voice says, I can hear the voice: IF YOU VALUE YOUR LIFE UNDERNEATH IT ALL YOU WILL OBEY WITHOUT QUESTION . . . the unspokenness . . . evil.

I get up and caress the young girl. She doesn't move. She moves from one foot to the other. She says: Are you begging? No one can afford you. But . . . but SHE is begging. She is holding out a begging bowl . . .

I pour the rest of the bottle into my face . . . the men are walking round the gardens now to keep themselves warm . . . I smash the bottle of spirit on the path . . . unsettle the birds and wake them. A strange aroma descends. Soon it will be dawn. The men are unaware of what I have been thinking . . . the face of Satan coming directly for them. I make the sign of the cross upside down . . .

Well?

MacGuinness looked up at the voice.

Well, said the police officer.

Hello whack, said MacGuinness.

What are you doing?

I am dictating my secret personality into a taping machine. There are a million reasons for spitting in the street and when you discover the right one, you can knock the street down . . .

Never mind about that, who does the machine belong to, and what's this broken bottle.

It's for bedsores . . . surgical spirit, a common or garden cure for bedsores, said MacGuinness.

Where's the bed?

Lomas came up and explained away the tape recorder. The police officer was convinced but threw them out of the gardens. They went into the Temple tube station, bought some threepenny tickets, Lomas and Cafferty got off at Charing Cross, and MacGuinness went round and round the Inner Circle all day.

* * * * *

Lomas played the tape of MacGuinness in the gardens to a medical friend of his, Mr. Martin. Mr. Martin said that the effect this man has created is clearly intentional. The cannabis, or marijuana, or the brown leaf of the graveyard as he calls it, which you say he was smoking, would not, although it is an hallucinogen, be sufficient to counteract the deadening of the frontal lobes produced by the barbiturates and the alcohol. It wouldn't be sufficient to produce the visual and auditory distortions which he seems to be trying to record on the tape: the statues coming to life, the voices, and so on. This man, I would say, is a dying race; and a second point is that barbiturates in such a dangerous quantity ups the toxicative quality of the surgical spirit, which is, of course, pure alcohol, by thirty per cent at least.

MacGuinness did not come into the park for two weeks. Tommy Ashe said that he was in the Colindale Hospital with T.B. He wasn't. Freddie Kilennen said that he was back in the mad house . . . somebody had said so, but twenty eight days went by. Perhaps he's been certified, said Lomas, he has been once, and then Betty got him out. He hadn't been.

Four weeks passed. Frankie Dillon who keeps the fruit barrow outside Fortes said he was dead.

After five weeks speeches began to be prefaced with memories of MacGuinness: how he was bred as the successor to Bonar Thompson the great speaker of the thirties, and how he had died unwanted, undernourished and drugged up right in the park, in full view of the crowds he had earlier swayed by his wit.

Six weeks passed. The rumours were authenticated by more people. The woman at the *Town and County* refreshment stand said that he had died of drugs in the park, and that she knew someone who had been to the funeral at Kensal Green where he was buried in a common grave. She said that he had forced his body to stand up to more than the human frame could stand, and he was only five foot two. Perhaps, she said, it was a blessing. It put him out of his misery.

Seven weeks passed. Cafferty had been accusing Lomas of being responsible. Lomas just shrugged his shoulders and said that if you sell yourself as a bundle of festive lunacy to the tourists week after week, you're bound to get infected sooner or later.

MacGuinness, said Lomas, had a drab obsession that he was a genius, and that his body was too small to carry it, so he had to set about destroying it. There is no room in MacGuinness for MacGuinness, all that drek. And anyway, he's got to die young . . .

Young? said Cafferty.

Well, to me he's young, said Lomas. He's got to die young to please the public. The trouble is that he hasn't left much of his genius behind him for them to play about with.

There are the articles in the *Irish Digest*, said Freddie Kilennen.

Yes, said Cafferty.

The rumours changed. MacGuinness was thought to be in Brixton prison. The dull epitaphs were wound up. Cafferty went to Brixton.

What do you want?

I'm a friend of William MacGuinness. I was told by . . .

Who by?

A man called . . .

We can't disclose any information, I'm sorry. Wait here. The warder closed the green door in the corner of the gates for eight minutes.

Come in. Come into the lodge. Now, you say you are a friend of this MacGuinness, well, how are we to know? If you were a wife or something like that, we might be able to do something. You see, if you can prove that he told you, by a letter or somesuch that he was here, then we'd be able to tell you whether he was here or not.

He's only allowed one letter a week, said Cafferty, and I expect he sends that to Betty, that's the woman who's looked after him sometimes . . .

Can't help you then, said the warder, showing Cafferty out of the lodge, and glancing possessively at the barred gates beyond the lodge. You see, that's the last right we give the prisoners . . . privacy.

Well, have you got a match? said Cafferty, flicking an unlit cigarette that hung from his lips.

No, said the warder. Never use them.

You must have been tempted.

What did you do then? said Freddie Kilennen.

Well, said Cafferty, the fact that he had taken the trouble to investigate the position suggested that MacGuinness was there, and his inviting me to the lodge was his undoing. The prison lodge telephone numbers are not for publication so I noted it down and I settled the matter from a telephone box on Brixton Hill. I have an authoritative voice at times.

Cafferty wrote to MacGuinness, care of the prison. A letter came back:

In replying to this letter, please write on the envelope:
Number 11437   Name: MacGuinness. W.P.   H.M. PRISON
                                             JEBB AVENUE
                                             BRIXTON S.W.2

2.11.63
My dear Son,
    Thank you for your letter, I know you can't read very fast, so I'm not going to write this letter very quick. As you will have noticed by

the above address I am back in my winter quarters, the Irish Riviera. I was arrested in Soho and charged with Sus. It is a frame up. I was blocked up on the tablets and wandering round tapping shop windows with a twig. They said it was loitering with intent. The intent was all theirs. I was found guilty and got three months, and they had a warrant out for me for not paying the £4 10s. fine for conducting that protest meeting outside Eveline's against her landlord, and I also got a week on top for nicking those three books, the ones on engineering. It was breach of probation.

But don't worry, it's not too bad inside. At least we have central heating, three meals a day and a good warm bed.

I am working in the mattress shop. It is cushy. Three of the lads from the Sally are doing time here, so I am not alone.

This hotel is packed for the winter season. Three in a cell. My two cell mates are two of the best a man could hope to meet in a day's walk.

We have a noisy bastard in the cell above. We are convinced that he is playing bowls with the piss pots or else it is shove halfpenny with the chairs.

I share the peter with Samuel Sam who is an ex-Cockney dosser who has been on the road most of his life. He has a gypsy daughter. One of the Jones's.

Yours, till a blade of grass become a tree,

Billy.

P.S. I come out on January the 8th. Meet me. 8 o'clock.

Eight o'clock, January the eighth. The gates opened and a few prisoners walked out. The light was jaundiced, the wind cold. The door half closed again and then re-opened, and MacGuinness stepped out, shaking hands with the warder.

Bye bye, love. The gates closed. He wiped the hand he had just shaken the warder's hand with, down the side of his trousers.

Hello son, how are you? filthy ponce . . . they're all QUEER in there. I went in crooked and came out bent. When's the off licence open? Where can we pick up some charge? . . . they're all

QUEER in there. Van Gogh cut his right ear off and he was still
starving for a bit of the other.

Don't look at me, said Cafferty. It's the law of the jungle, the
cookie's gotta crumble . . .

Yes . . . yes, said MacGuinness. What do we do now? Where
the hell are we anyway? They brought me here blindfolded so I
wouldn't know where it was to come again. That is sociology.
Let's catch a bus.

There was a bus going to the Oval. He said goodbye to his
fellow prisoners, saying that he'd look them up again some time
and telling them to say one thing, think the other and do the
opposite to both.

MacGuinness and Cafferty got into the bus. He turned and
stared at a woman in the seat behind:

There's an old chinese proverb, lady, said MacGuinness,
Heroes have no manners. How are you? nice to see you here.
They could do NOTHING to me in there. Look at the FAT
on me . . .

He stood up in his seat and tucked his waistband under his
stomach so that it stuck out. The woman looked out of the
window. MacGuinness sat down again and turned to Cafferty:

They have got the idea in there that everyone wants to eat, and
they impose it on you. How do you like the gear? it's the same as
I went in with, smells the same . . . except for the belt and the
socks, which I robbed from the store. I was a model prisoner: red
band on the bathhouse after they transferred me from the
mattresses. They trusted me. When they transferred me from the
bathhouse to the store, I made fifty pairs of pants go round five
hundred prisoners: they bloody well had to trust me. I've got
the rest on.

He pulled out all the letters he had been given on his release,
addressed to the Labour Exchange, Prisoners Welfare and the
National Assistance Board and tore them open:

'. . . on discharge he had £-s-d private cash and was given

£-s-d release money. Address to which proceeding on discharge: Room required . . .' and listen to this. 'To the Manager, Ministry of Labour, Peckham: . . . Mr. MacGuinness is desirous of obtaining employment in your area. I am writing personally about Mr. MacGuinness to save him possible embarrassment when he arrives at your office . . .' it's a stereotyped letter. 'yours faithfully Welfare Officer' that was the only woman in the place . . . terrible ugly. The longer I was there, the more I got to like her. That's terrible.

He turned round again and stared at the woman behind.

We've got to get to Peckham son. I plan to live there . . . pack-in the park. Tell you about it later.

They changed at the Oval and got into the tube:

Let us join the ladies, said MacGuinness, sitting opposite two office cleaners. They could do NOTHING to MacGuinness. MacGuinness is adaptable; that suit of mine over at Bet's place: that cost thirty five quid. MacGuinness is adaptable. Mac-Guinness was the only man the governor could talk to. He came down to the bathhouse where I was, and said to me: what's the significance of the ear-rings? (I was wearing two at the time . . . said it was against my religion to take them off.) So I said, when a child is born to be king they put an ear-ring in, and when he IS the king, then he wears two. So he says: the king's not setting a very good example, is he? What are you doing in prison? So I said to him: What are you doing in prison? The only difference is that you have two prison officers at the back of you, whereas I can dig all the brains in the nick. He said: I've never seen it that way before.

But you've got to establish your toughness . . . One of the screws came up to me and said: What happened to your teeth? So I told him; I said I wore them out making love . . . He got really vicious, said he'd bring his baton straight over my head. Darling, I said, I've never had it that way before. What could the poor man do? He was paralysed . . . said Hitler did away with

six million of me in the last war . . . there was madness in his eyes.
But I stopped. I was seeing the madness of my own eyes, in his . . .

Peckham. MacGuinness looked through his papers and found
the address of a man he'd been recommended to see about a room
while he was inside.

The man's name is Barnes, he said, drawing out the vowel.
Baaaarnes. That's a name to start a revolution with. Let's go.

Mr. Barnes gave MacGuinness a room.

Could you spare us a bit of the gas money on the mantelpiece?
said MacGuinness. We've to get to the National Assistance . . .
Are you a junky? Do you get high on shoving the gas ring into
a saucepan of milk and letting it percolate and drinking it?

No, said Mr. Barnes.

Then you won't be needing the gas money.

Name? said the man at the National Assistance.

MacGuinness. You spell it as you drink it.

Do you have a room in Peckham?

I do, and here are the papers. He produced a piece of paper with
Barnes's address on it, and the letters from the prison.

I see, Mr. MacGuinness. Do you intend staying in Peckham for
long?

I do, said MacGuinness. I have smelt the place out and found
that Peckham is a heavily employed area, and that always means
an understanding National Assistance Board.

I see. What is your normal sort of employment, Mr. Mac-
Guinness?

Thief.

I'm afraid I can't put that down.

Then put down: giving interviews.

Well, what sort of WORK have you done?

None. I'm too heavy for light work, too light for heavy work,
and too sexy for night work.

Three pounds one shilling and a penny. Sign here . . .

What about my son? said MacGuinness pointing at Cafferty. He is an idiot, an imbecile. I have to do everything for him. He would tear the place apart, if it wasn't for me. Look at him. He's a half starved wreck, a dying lunatic.

That's right, said Cafferty. And I have a porous leg.

Maybe, but you're no relation of his. Three pounds one and a penny, sign here.

The money was spent in the *World Turned Upside Down* in the Old Kent Road, because MacGuinness said that he had once begun a book there called *Convention Be Damned* with the title inverted.

I also began another. It started off: A man walked into my mind and said F you MacGuinness, and walked out again. Some old tart tore it up on me . . .

He sat down contemplative, with one hand in his waistband and the other turning the ear-ring slowly round in his ear lobe:

Are they queuing up for me in the park? . . . you remember the bouncer outside the Greek club? he was inside for poncing. As soon as I arrived, he said: MacGuinness The King, and I was king from then on. MacGuinness had them all marching in step with MacGuinness in the exercise yard, when the screw said that MacGuinness was out of step. I got them all blocked to hell every night with the alcohol from the Brasso. You strain it four times. Then they transferred me to the kitchen, and I got them all blocked up on gas and milk . . . They kept telling me in there that I was a social problem. I was so happy in there that the screws were discontented. THEY were the social problem . . . Grainger from the Sally, he was there, and Campbell for a week. Terrible gumboil he had . . . until some Christian steamer bailed him out.

All QUEER in there, even the screws . . . Mrs. Smith and Mrs. White are now coming down the corridor to check on the emptying of the piss pots of Mrs. Aly Khan and Mrs. Mac-Guinness. . . . I shouted at the screw in the exercise yard: DON'T

TOUCH HER SHE'S MINE. She didn't even blush . . . Where
do we go now? you're going? finish the crater, finish the crater.
Never get behind hand with your beer, it catches up with you in
the end. Thanks for the letter you sent me in the nick. I didn't
understand a word of it. That poem it ended up with, who wrote
it? Stroke the golden cockatoo, see how deep your fingers go . . .
the screws censored it with their censorship scissors. Cut out part
of the last word of the first line. But I could see what it was.

He pulled the letter from his pocket. It looked like a mat of
paper lace.

He went back to the room in Peckham and stayed there in bed
refusing to come back to the park. Cafferty went to see him
again.

He was lying in the bed which was strewn with apple cores and
bread crusts, and he was eating stale flakes out of the torn stub of
a cereal packet:

I tore off the back of it to win the competition. They wanted a
hundred words on why I like their produce, and they were going
to use it as an advertisement. I took the opportunity to let them
know what I thought of advertising. Have you a threepenny
stamp to send it off with? he said, pointing to the torn back of the
cereal packet on the floor.

Cafferty picked it up. MacGuinness had written all over it:

Why should I advertise you? Why should I advertise anyone?
EVERY SIXPENNY BAR OF OUR SOAP CONTAINS A
PINT AND A HALF OF FRESH MILK. Now let us examine
that. A pint of milk in London today will cost you eightpence
halfpenny. Therefore a pint and a half of milk will cost you a
shilling three farthings. In a sixpenny bar of soap you are asked
to believe that you are getting a shilling and three farthings'
worth of milk. I myself have strived for three nights running to
get a pint and a half of milk into one of those bars of soap. The
milk was flowing downstairs. The landlady had her suspicions.
My name is MacGuinness.

He took it from Cafferty's hands and tore it up slowly.

I'll tell you, he said, why I'm packing up speaking in the park. MacGuinness is tired of trying to find himself. I am in everyone's subconscious through speaking in that park, and that's neither the way to find yourself or lose yourself, but when MacGuinness walks down the street he meets MacGuinness going up it. MacGuinness is his own son avenging his own father. When they listen to me in the park, when I'm drugged up, when Lomas has me jabbering on the tape recorder about my daughter in Galway in the form of a statue, that is the old MacGuinness being echoed by the old MacGuinness. MacGuinness the madman.

Who is the new MacGuinness? said Cafferty.

Up to now MacGuinness has been getting pennies, now MacGuinness is going to get the pounds. MacGuinness has dug the criminal mind. Can I borrow your crombie coat for a couple of days? I could get anything with a crombie coat. I've got to have a front. Are you with that? I've got to have a front. MacGuinness wants folder money and since MacGuinness has been in the nick and dug the criminal mind, he knows where it is and he's going to get it. They think their pound notes are God, and MacGuinness is going to turn them into atheists.

There's sexuality in thieving, there's sexuality in speaking . . . but there's the dark female scheming sexuality in the thieving mind. That's why all the thieves are queer. MacGuinness went into Brixton innocent and MacGuinness has come out guilty . . . MacGuinness has dug the criminal mind.

He got up and stood at the window.

I'm going to get a pair of white silk women's gloves, because they're more flexible . . .

Cafferty said that it seemed a good idea apart from the bit about the crombie coat. Mr. Barnes came in and asked Mac-Guinness for the rent.

Have you any money? said MacGuinness turning to Cafferty.

Half a sheet, said Cafferty.

He means ten shillings, said MacGuinness taking it from Cafferty. He wants to disguise the fact that it's filthy money. It's all of ten shillings. Will it make you happy Mr. Barnes? I mean no man has the right to be happy, so take it with a guilty look on your face.

Mr. Barnes took it and left the room.

Why did that happen? said Cafferty.

He owes money to someone in the nick.

Well that someone is in the nick, isn't he?

He is, said MacGuinness, but not for long. There was a tobacco putsch in the nick and I came out on top, and I came out on top as I was a red band prisoner with a greater tobacco allowance, along with the fellow he owes the money to. . . .

Get away, said Cafferty. Brixton is only a short term nick.

MacGuinness ignored him, and went on: MacGuinness is crooked and MacGuinness is going that crooked that the police won't recognize him any more, and I'm not just bumming my chat . . . bumming my load . . . bragging. I mean it. Can I have the crombie coat for the front?

All right, said Cafferty, all right. I'll see you in the park.

You can't combine being a professional thief with speaking in that park, said MacGuinness. You've got to sink away . . . there's one other ambition I want to tell you about . . . I was dreaming it up when I was in the nick. You know when you stare at the people passing in the street? there's one eye that you can't catch, and that's a Chinaman's. . . .

Three weeks passed. MacGuinness never came into the park.

Have you seen MacGuinness? said Freddie Kilennen.

I have, said Cafferty. He's in Peckham, planning a bank robbery . . .

Get away, said Freddie Kilennen. He'll be back on the drugs. He was blocked up to hell in the nick wasn't he? then he'll be blocked up now.

I don't think so, said Cafferty.

He needs them, said Freddie Kilennen, to insulate himself against the outside world.

Against his own egocentricity, said Cafferty, leaving him and crossing the road into Fortes. He sat down, looked in the mirror in front of him and saw MacGuinness reading some woman's hand behind him:

At exactly twenty one years of age, MacGuinness was saying, you will be at the cross roads of life. On that day of that minute of that hour, you will realize that there are three sides to a story: your side, your husband's side and the facts. I can read you like a book darling. The trouble is I wouldn't be able to shut you up as quick . . . Pay your fare.

Cafferty went over. MacGuinness was not wearing the crombie coat.

Hello.

Hello whack . . .

What happened to the front?

The front? said MacGuinness, Oh, the crombie . . . it's down the Sally, down in Lisson Street, I'm back there now. You're not offended about the coat? I mean, take my advice: there are no monkeys on my back, I'm on the bloody monkey's back.

MacGuinness got up, thanked the woman whose hand he'd been reading for the money she had given him, and went to another stool.

Are you blocked? said Cafferty.

I've been speaking in the park, so I'm blocked.

I didn't know you'd been speaking.

Well, I couldn't keep them waiting any longer.

You look ill.

You are seeing yourself in my eyes.

A man came up to him:

Have you any? said MacGuinness.

A few . . . four purple hearts and a bomber.

How much do you want?

Five shillings.

Right.

The man passed them across the counter under his hand, and said: I'll see you tomorrow. If I see you I see you, if I don't I don't.

Don't talk that way, said MacGuinness. I'll be outside the Salvation Army hostel in Lisson Street at nine o'clock tomorrow morning . . .

The man left.

Notice how he's picked up all the sophisticated English expressions, said MacGuinness. If I see you I see you . . . Did you notice the slit eyes? Did you notice them? He's Chinese . . . Chinese. It's an argument for something, I've forgotten what . . .

He swilled down the tablets: amphetomene and methedrine, with a bottle of tonic wine:

I don't have to come back to this earth until Wednesday morning when I sign on and get my money . . .

He waited for the deadening of the frontal lobes, and then shut up.

I heard MacGuinness speaking in the park today, said Lomas. Usual drek: When I came over here to make my second million pound, every lavatory cleaner in England is a frustrated journalist, and . . .

Did he mention Brixton? said Cafferty.

No, said Lomas. No, he didn't tell them where he'd been. Kept it back. It must have been a bit of a strain, he always makes anything like that part of his equipment. No, he just stuck to the usual stuff: how he was sent over here by the Irish Republican Army to elevate English intelligence to a lower level of thinking, and MacGuinness this and MacGuinness this, MacGuinness that, MacGuinness this, MacGuinness that, MacGuinness, MacGuinness, MacGuinness. . . .

.   .   .   .   .

There's a species of large worm, Lomas went on, which begins to eat its tail, if it's coiled itself up carelessly and the tail happens to be in front of its mouth. That is the ultimate in egocentricity. MacGuinness has a long way to go.

I don't know about that, said Cafferty.

All sorrow is linked . . . all sorrow is linked.

Axel Ney Hoch

WHAT IS THE FUNDAMENTAL TRUTH? it is simply that we are PEOPLE, and as such we are like the people who live in Russia, the people who live in Africa, the people who live in China . . . racially and genetically INDIVISIBLE. We are ONE PEOPLE . . . ONE KIND . . . and they PROFIT by our division and our hyphenation . . . those who profit by war and the fear of war, and mass thinking and group prejudice. For GOD'S SAKE exercise that healthy element of hatred if you wish, but take this precaution at least: BE INTRODUCED to the subject of your spite and venom . . . KNOW the man you hate, KNOW the woman you hate and THEN kill her . . . kill him, or worse still educate him.

But don't have group prejudice. Group prejudice is SILLY . . . and group prejudice is exploited by those who inflict it upon you . . . EVANS WAS HANGED! He made a written confession. He was ILLITERATE. He could not read. He could not write. They TAUGHT him to read and write in the charge room, and then they broke his neck . . . and WHAT DID YOU DO ABOUT IT? WHAT DID YOU DO? you dynamic people. . . . Judges rule: PUT MEN AWAY FOR LIFE . . . HAVE THEM

EXECUTED! You can have people's spines broken in England
. . . HERE! NOT in horrible Russia, NOT in wicked Germany,
but HERE in TEA SOAKED, FISHEYED, SLOPPY, HALF
DEAD, ARTIFICIAL, PIDDLING ENGLAND. . . .

What did you do, when, the other day, in the *Daily Express*,
Lord Shawcross, late Attorney General of the CROWN of
ENGLAND, announced that there were hundreds of men and
women INNOCENTLY INCARCERATED in British prisons
because they could not afford to have their cases brought for
rehearing in the House of Lords, which is YOUR HIGHEST
COURT HOUSE, you muck race . . . IT IS YOUR HIGHEST
COURT OF LAW! It is the House of Lords . . . the house of
dandies, all dressed in long silk stockings and royal garters,
keeping their cobblers' thread in a hand knitted cosy . . . these
apologies for women, who shuffle about on their syphilitic
behinds in establishments of privilege and vice. THEY ARE
YOUR HIGHEST JUDGES! THEY RULE YOU! And you
kid yourselves, you kid yourselves that by putting the mark of
illiteracy on a piece of paper that you will determine how you
will live? Go to court and see a poor man jailed for six months
and a rich woman let off from stealing by paying for an army of
psychologists to say that her mother dragged her off a chamber
pot too early.

WHY, ladies and gentlemen, WHY is the scientific sustaining
of useless lives good, and the scientific control of non-existent
lives evil?

Why are masses of men and women herded together in vast
cyst cities, frustrated in their attempts to find fulfilment in their
lives?

Why are they categorized? Why are they classified? Why are
they separated? Why is their anger and their personal bitterness
channelled into patriotic anger?

The implication of the anti-fraternization law was that the
people WANTED to be friends. . . . Group hatred is AN EN-

TIRELY ARTIFICIAL CREATION, it is artificially created, artificially maintained and artificially exploited by politicians.

The solution to a cancer is to CUT IT OUT! The solution to tyranny is to OPPOSE IT! . . . SITTING DOWN . . . LYING DOWN . . . FIGHTING . . . STANDING . . . RUN-NING . . . JUMPING . . . BY ALL MEANS . . . for the state torments you BY . . . ALL . . . MEANS . . .

That is Axel, said Lomas.

Yes, said Cafferty.

He is styled the Zarathustra of the Latter Days, Lomas said. He's a quarter German, quarter Jewish, quarter Russian, and the other quarter accounted for by places, times or emotions. During the war, to escape from Germany, he was Polish; and now, I believe, he's officially Stateless.

I remember a Jewish friend of his, Louis, you've seen him around. . . . I remember him coming up to Axel after a meeting and saying that Axel was the only German anti-fascist, Jewish anti-semite and Russian anti-communist that he knew, and that he was quite pleased to know him. Axel said that he was quite pleased to know Louis too, but that these characteristics were just variations on being English which he felt accounted for the other quarter when he was with Louis.

Why does he speak? said Cafferty.

I'm not absolutely sure, Lomas said.

Axel is a large man, dressed in army shirts, cardigans, several sweaters and a large donkey jacket with the cloth frayed and the dye worn away at the elbows and seams. He sheds them down to the shirts as he speaks. Underneath it all is a pair of overalls tucked into a pair of high black boots in such a way as to leave the knees emphatic.

He comes into the park on a motor cycle, leaves it off the Edgware Road and strides onto the tarmac, stopping to listen to the other speakers, talk to people that he knows, hugging them or clasping their hands for a long while. His eyelids hang like padded bolsters round his eyes making them smile permanently if they are visible. The effect is of rows of fat creases that ripple up and down, obscuring asiatic eyes as the cheek muscles tighten.

He is genial, Lomas said, because he listens to the other speakers, which is rare, and he is the only speaker who has never been paid to speak, and who's never taken a collection inside or outside the gates. He's spoken for very few causes, and the ones he's spoken for, he's only abandoned them when he felt their objects were realized. Zionism, for example, he abandoned on the formation of the state of Israel.

What about the Displaced Persons? said Freddie Kilennen. He used to speak for them dear.

I suppose, Lomas said, that he felt there weren't any more of them. None anyway that began with capital letters . . . And I'll tell you another thing, Cafferty. He differs from the other speakers in another way. Although you know it's Axel speaking, the platform revolves round the subject matter and not himself. I think that's why he doesn't refer to himself as Axel, in the third person, on the platform, like some of the others do. He uses the word 'I', but he uses it geographically, to put the crowd in a position they might be in.

That's right, said Freddie Kilennen, he's not an egotist.

I remember once, Lomas went on, he was attacking the immorality of the parking regulations in the West End . . . he's quite well off I think, he has a car. Well, he started it off by describing an incident of how he took a child with a hole in her heart, a child suffering from a heart disease who hadn't long to live, to a show for little children off Old Compton Street, and he parked the car. . . . I can't remember how it went on, but that child was his own. I happen to know; and he kept it from the crowd. His identity is only illustrative in his speaking and not the ultimate point of it.

That is the sign of a mature speaker, said Freddie Kilennen.

They got up from the table, left the *New Inn*, and went over to the park where Axel was speaking from his step ladder by the railings that divide the park from Park Lane.

He was being heckled by a man who haunts his meetings, a strange looking man with a drawn face, dressed in a grey onanist raincoat with catacombs of repression locked inside. He haunts no one else's meetings, only Axel's, and shouts small speeches at him from a guarded position behind the railings in a savage military accent.

The point is this, the man was saying, the majority of people are enslaved and always HAVE been enslaved, because they are slaves mentally. Does this fellow with his shouting and bawling on the platform have any actual effect on the audience besides amusement? I would say NO. He has nothing POSITIVE to offer and what the people want is something POSITIVE. All right, so they get tired with being fed with flags and the traditional rubbish, but still they want to be fed with SOMETHING. Of course they do and this fellow has nothing to offer them . . .

Axel was listening to him from the platform, and then he quietly got down went over to him and offered him the platform. The man came round from the other side of the railings, climbed up and went on in the same vein.

You see what I mean, said Lomas. He attaches no importance to the platform.

That is because he has a platform manner on or off the platform, said Freddie Kilennen.

Cafferty went up to Axel as he came out of the crowd and asked him why he gave up his platform to people like that:

Mostly because I'm tired, said Axel walking over to the refreshment stall. He only interrupts me because he wants to speak. He always used to heckle me until I got him to speak. I find that this way I can channel his disturbing influence. While I'm off the platform he can exhaust himself . . . Do you want some tea?

You see, speaking on the platform when you have internal injuries is very painful. Supposing you were carrying some great weight on your head and some silly little joker comes along and tickles you, well you'd be terribly tempted to say: Here, you take this. The audience usually hates him for it, whereas, as long as he's a heckler they're entirely on his side, because this is the traditional position: to side with a heckler. He's really funny. He's the iconoclast. He's knocking down the big boy. But by putting him on the platform, I'm doing two things. I'm exposing him as an indifferent speaker, and at the same time I'm giving myself a cheap holiday. It stops them. I've had many many people heckling me and I put them on a platform and they don't heckle me any more, they regard me as a friend. They wait patiently until I say: Would you like to speak? and then along they come, you see. They pretend they need to be pushed, but I know they're waiting for it, you see. Then I go away and I've got somebody to look after my platform.

Don't you understand? Suppose you walked about with a platform and asked several people, saying: Excuse me, would you mind looking after this? they wouldn't dream of it, but stand them on a platform and say: Would you SPEAK? . . . Oh! they say, I ACCEPT YOUR CHALLENGE. While they're there I can go away, have a meal, have a drink, and when I come back there's the platform, and I say: Excuse me, can I ask a question? and they say: Yes, what is it? and I say: Excuse me, can I have my platform please?

I see, Cafferty said.

You see, look, there are two possibilities, either he is no good, in which case being on the platform is a punishment, and the audience feels all the more sympathetic towards me. They say: Oh, what a nice fellow he is giving his platform to this silly sod . . . Oh, he's far too generous. Or, on the other hand, he's a good speaker, but again I win because the audience say: Ah, wasn't it good of him to let this funny fellow speak, because we'd much

sooner listen to him . . . oh, it WAS nice of the other fellow to
give way. He's not ambitious, he SHARES things, he's A NICE
fellow. You see? So both ways I win, and in the third way I win
too, because I get a holiday. When you speak for hours on end,
you just can't go on being witty and eloquent. There must come a
time when the second house starts and you have to start at the
beginning again.

He dropped his cardboard tea cup into the litter bin and walked
back into the middle of his crowd. Cafferty stayed on the outside.
The heckler climbed down, and Axel climbed up again.

His speaking style in the park is loud, gestured and sometimes
tearful. He sits hunched on the stepladder hanging over the heads
of the crowd with the tips of his fingers and thumbs touching
and the hands throbbing up and down as a sign of histrionic
incredulity. He stands upright clutching the bar of the steps and
only moving his head.

Lomas and Freddie Kilennen came over to where Cafferty was
standing.

Those are actions which he can't escape from, Lomas said. They
are actions which dictate a form of expression. You see . . . watch
him now, his arms are stiffened in the air. He seems to want the
words to become a physical structure above him to defend the
inadequacy of his gestures.

That's right in a way, Cafferty, said Freddie Kilennen.

They moved further into the crowd to hear better:

When Queen Agatha the Monolithic of Luxembourg comes
here on a state visit to open a public lavatory, DON'T wave
your flags, DON'T assassinate her. He who assassinates her as he
who crowned her is an idolator. THROW these people into the
bed that belongs to them . . . they are ORDINARY. They are
only elevated out of the ordinary by our SUB ORDINARINESS
. . . these people are only elevated above your condition when
you make yourself tiny.

It is not a doctor's job to foresee a time when there will be no sickness; it is a doctor's job to fight sickness wherever he finds it. Don't speak of absolutes. DON'T look forward to the stateless society. Look forward to living among men and women who will fight the evils of the state that have sorrowed their being, and WHITTLE THEM AWAY . . . piecemeal . . . BIT . . . BY . . . BIT . . . BY . . . BIT. Unless of course you want a community which spends its time sitting on its arse drinking cold water out of vacuum flasks on Hampstead Heath fasting for the pygmies of Zanzibar. WHAT A LOT OF UNADULTERATED COBB-LERS when half the pygmies of Zanzibar are living in London . . .

BREATHE FRESH AIR INTO THEIR FACES! they are fat, USELESS COBBLERS! that is the way to treat the upper classes. And if you go to jail for it . . . GO TO JAIL AND SET THE PLACE ON FIRE . . . BURN IT DOWN!

When they violate your intellectual principles, then contradict them intellectually, and when they assault you emotionally, put on a gramophone record of the *Song of the Steppes*. And when they assault you by violence . . . DEFEND YOURSELVES BY VIOLENCE! the only way to get rid of the jails in England is to tear them down, brick by brick, and when there aren't enough heroic people left in England to get rid of these infamous citadels of dirt and shame . . . but, we AREN'T a society of heroes, this is a society of specialists who do little things to little noughts which they twist up and lick. This is a society of dollies and paper dummies, all brought up on little biscuits with enormous pictures on the wall of inflated and diseased mammary glands. . . .

Cafferty listened to him for several weeks and found that he had some more specific attitudes; on the day of the Royal Birthday, he said this:

Today is a very important day. Today is the official birthday. We also have an unofficial birthday and a semi-official birthday. The year is filled with this kind of thing. When I come here tomorrow there'll be five hundred guns lined up here and they'll all go BOOOOOOOOOOOM. I myself am going to buy a can of beans and a market garden to celebrate this happy event.

Of the army, he said this:

Go to Buckingham Palace and see them standing out there like petrified candlesticks. I ask you? is this the instinct of a man? or the instinct of a peanut? It is the instinct of a vegetable . . . to lie about and be cut down when the time comes.

This was Axel on the police:

They talk about going to Moscow and burning it down because Moscow they say is a police state. They've got long distance heroism. WHAT A LOT OF COBBLERS . . . you can't go down Oxford Street with a walking stick and a piece of lead at the end. If you took your girl friend to pieces last time and a copper finds a piece of elastic in your pocket, you'll be done for carrying a catapult. You're not ALLOWED to be violent. You're not allowed to say NO to the police state. Of course you're not, and you acquiesce to it.

And on lies:

The newspapers never say WE HAVE LIED, WE HAVE DECEIVED THE PEOPLE. If they do have to print an apology, it's written underneath the football pool coupon on the back page. It is lost in the limbo of the dustbin arrangements of the sports page. We live in a land ruled by liars, governed by liars and publicized by liars. The solution is pornocricide, to end the sorrow of the man filling in the coupon on the back page to earn the filth on the front. If you want your children to grow up rich and powerful then teach them to tell a colourful lie. If they are honest, then as soon as they go to school they'll ask questions about religion, and if they ask questions about religion they become personas non grata; they won't be allowed to attend, they'll be tormented, they'll be forced to join various minority groups and go to funny schools and eventually finish up being locked up for having shouted the word Peace outside the War Office.

On fashion:

Fashion isn't very dangerous. If you want to be uncomfortable and wear a tie, there's nothing I can do for you. And if you're a lady and decide to get yourself stuck together with sticky plaster and covered in chemistry and whalebones and some artificial mish mash or the other, well there you are, there's very little you can do, except have a gay time with the girl taking her to bits.

And on war:

YOU CANNOT CONTRACT OUT OF WAR. You cannot contract out of the status quo because you are too WEAK. You have delegated all your violence, all your romance, all your glamour to the image of the state which it spews upon you. You have NO freedom. When they want you in the army, they TAKE you. Would you like to vote for war today dear? would you like to vote to go to Cyprus and have your cobblers shot off? would you like to vote dear, to have your sisters and mothers bombed for six bloody years with a pause for tea and time to paint your legs because I'm afraid we've run out of stockings?

When the Kaiser went to war with Lloyd George they weren't fighting because they loved the German people or because they loved the British people, but they loved to go on EXPLOITING the people they had been exploiting, and they wanted to GO ON AND THEY WANTED TO EXTEND THE FIELD OF EXPLOITATION . . . That's why they fought each other, and not because they wanted to exchange their fields of love. That's the world we live in. Sometimes an enemy is so big that like little children we cut off our heads and say I'm not here.

He has also recently become very Anti-American, Lomas said. I remember last week there was an American in the crowd who was getting under his skin and he said . . . what was it? yes . . . America is a mish mash of genetic goulash. I hope that you will go to England to have your soul educated. I hope that you will go

to Germany to have your emotions educated. I hope that you go
to Holland and get drowned. But before wipe off whatever
advertisements you have embroidered on your clothes.

There was a reason for that, said Cafferty. I asked him about
it.

You've got to know him, then? said Lomas.

A little, Cafferty said. But the reason was that an American
tourist came up to Axel a couple of weeks ago and said that he
was impressed by his speaking but that he felt that Axel had
unfortunate ideas about America which he could cure by
arranging a lecture tour for him, with radio and television
appearances, hotel bills paid and lectures in every state, and so on.
Well apparently this made Axel believe in himself as a saleable
commodity . . .

It would, said Lomas.

And the next day he went down to Bernard Shaw's house in
Ayot St. Lawrence, Cafferty went on, he often goes there, I
think he admires Bernard Shaw. And he wrote the American a
letter on Bernard Shaw's typewriter, which he pointed out that
he was using. He accepted the invitation, and also explained to
the man that he was a vegetarian, although it was irrelevant to the
question of the lecture tour; but Axel thought it relevant to the
fact that he was using Bernard Shaw's typewriter. This letter
came back. Axel gave it to me.

Read it out then, Lomas said.

It's from *Lambert Huffman, Publishers, Winover, Indiana. Dear
Mr. Ney*, it says, *I regret to tell you that my sponsorship of your coming
to the United States has been denied by my business and editorial
associates on whom I must have relied to complete the arrangements and
carry through the projects we had in mind. In this meat packing and
meat eating centre of the world there is perhaps no one less welcome than
a vegetarian and especially an articulate vegetarian. It was the militancy
of your letter in this matter that earned for me the irrevocable opposition
against which I am powerless. Please forgive me for rousing hopes which*

*by the very nature of things at this late time now revealed could never
be realized. Respectfully, Lambert Huffman.*

They are always doing that sort of thing, Lomas said, offering
lecture tours to the speakers. They can't think of any other way
of getting into conversation with them.

Axel's vegetarianism floods into other contexts.

After a meeting while Cafferty was talking to Axel, a man
came up and invited them to a meal. The man had a car.

A very generous idea, Axel said.

Well, said the man, I was deeply moved by your speech, and
would be most interested to discuss some of your ideas with you.

Have you read Nietzsche and Schopenhauer? said Axel.

No, said the man.

Never mind. Let's go.

Axel entered Smiths through the shop entrance as he wanted
to buy some pickled cucumber.

I want to buy some pickled cucumber, he said to a German
woman behind the counter. He said it in German and the woman
explained that to sell pickled cucumber on a Sunday was a
contravention of the Shops Act 1950. Axel's German became
more expressive and he told the woman that pickled cucumber
was a perishable commodity and that Mr. Smith's pickled
cucumbers would be *tot* or dead on Monday.

Mr. Smith came across from the restaurant and intervened.
He informed Axel that it was not his fault and that an Enforce-
ment Officer patrolled the building at eight o'clock on Sundays
to ensure that pickled cucumbers and other items such as tea
which the law considered it unhealthy for the public to consume
on a Sunday were not sold in Smiths on that day. Axel bought
some Edgworth Flake tobacco and went into the restaurant. Mr.
Smith followed.

The man who was paying ordered a large mug of German beer,
and then another when it came. His eyes started to water and his

head started to roll until he managed to trap it in his hands. With his elbows on the table he trained his eyes into the bottom of the mug and remained silent. Axel ordered egg mayonnaise and potato salad. Mr. Smith stood at the table clutching an empty chair top with his fists, and Cafferty listened.

Mr. Smith, said Axel, if I brought a freshly cut lettuce into here would you be shocked?

No, said Mr. Smith.

But if I brought a freshly murdered pig into here, dragging it along the parquet floors, would you then be shocked?

I am a butcher, said Mr. Smith.

Axel paused, looked at the man who was paying, and went on:

But why is it, Mr. Smith, that like all herbivores you have long intestines? Why is it that like all herbivores you control your temperature through the pores of your skin? Why is it that unlike all carnivores you do not control your temperature through the tongue? Why is it that like all herbivores you are not equipped to catch the running beast, and . . .

But why do I have carnivorous teeth? said Mr. Smith.

That is a loaded question, Mr. Smith, said Axel. That is a loaded question: why have you got carnivorous teeth. This is like saying: when did you stop beating your wife? But listen to these questions, Mr. Smith, and then I will tell you the answers. . . . Why is it that in ninety nine cases out of a hundred of food poisoning the source of the poisoning has been discovered to be flesh? and why is it that the bacilli which attack vegetation do not survive in your intestines? Why is it that the bacilli which attack carrion . . . Why is it that your children, Mr. Smith, when they are born, have a natural abhorrence for flesh, whereas in nature, creatures whose parents eat flesh have a natural liking for it? Why is it that the butcher is not permitted to show his wares outside the windows of his shops but the greengrocer is? Why is it that in English law a butcher's evidence in capital cases was not accepted until the turn of the last century? WHY IS IT?

I will tell you, Mr. Smith . . . no, before I tell you, I want to warn you. You see, my principal objection to the carnivorous kind is not a medical one, it's a moral one, because I've already been converted to the idea that vegetarianism is healthier than carnivorosity by great physicians and dieticians whose pamphlets I would be pleased to present you with, Mr. Smith, if this gentleman is kind enough to bring me here next week. You see, so even if you could convince me that a flesh diet was not injurious to my health and my anatomy, nevertheless I would still oppose it because it is injurious to my mind.

Yes, said Mr. Smith.

The breeding of animals, Mr. Smith, for the slaughterer's knife is a gross immorality because you cannot eat flesh without being involved in gross torment and torture and pain. An animal is bred for the butcher's knife and is sold by weight, therefore the heavier a beast is, the more the middle man makes and the better the animal is stuffed the fatter it becomes, the more unhealthy its organs, the more money made in the transaction, the more toxic the substance presented to you on the table.

You may say, Mr. Smith, that they are just bodies, but you are just a body, Mr. Smith. Nobody can stand on your toe without assaulting your mind, you see. What is there but my body, when I am dumb and my spirit has been martyred? And when they fling me in, they do it with their bloody bodies. Nobody has ever been charged with shooting a spirit you know. . . .

In Germany, which you'll agree Mr. Smith, has a reputation second to none for cruelty and brutality against animals, geese are actually nailed to little wooden boards in order to produce a liver disease because it produces a succulent tasty sausage. And in England you have broiler calves which are kept in little boxes, never see daylight and never see each other, and at the economic point of no return they have their throats cut to bleed gradually the kosher way to produce pure white flesh. Then the rabbi comes along and says what have you, and it becomes holy flesh, and

then the Jewish housewife comes along and dips this lump of
sorrow into salt water for twelve hours, says another mumbo
jumbo, the name of the holy ghost and my auntie Clarissa and lo
and behold it has become bloodless . . . because the Talmud forbids
the consumption of blood. But if a pathologist at Scotland Yard
got hold of this lump of flesh, even if it had been immersed in salt
water for three years, he could still take from it particles of blood,
identify the blood group and tell you what the animal would
have died of if it had gone on living.

Your customers, Mr. Smith, are stuffing themselves with
secondhand dehydrated corpses. They're not like little predators,
they're not even killers. They're scavengers. They're stuffing
themselves with bits and pieces that are lying about and they're
turning their stomach into a cemetery. But nature, Mr. Smith,
nature is different. In nature it's necessary. If it weren't for the lion
and the beasts of prey, the animals they live on would be exterm-
inated by themselves. If the lion doesn't keep a herd of wildebeest
on the run, they will uproot all the grass and the soil will blow
away in the wind. They MUST be kept moving. The weak must
be kicked out and the weak ARE kicked out by the predators.
But you see, the predators don't enjoy it, they kill. Instantly.
They kill the weak, and the herds move on and because they move
on they survive. But that's not our way, is it Mr. Smith?

I suppose not, said Mr. Smith.

Our way is deliberately to breed animals . . . to feed them on
mountains of vegetables in order to make a little succulent dish of
sin . . . because flesh IS sin. That little question about the sins of
the flesh is obsolete. Flesh IS sin. And the people of the metropolis
of Berlin and the people of the metropolis of London and the
people of the metropolis of Paris, are indifferent to the slaughter
of other people because they are conditioned to the sight and
smell of corpses as they walk past their butchers' shops. I don't
represent vegetarianism, you see Mr. Smith. I just represent my
conscience.

We've just come from Hyde Park. . . .

Oh yes, said Mr. Smith.

Have you ever been to Marble Arch and seen that restaurant where they have hundreds of chickens, Mr. Smith, cruelly and INDECENTLY skewered through the behind by metal coated toothpicks revolving in the window? If you have a hundred chickens locked up in batteries, Mr. Smith, or if you have only got one and you tie it to the bedpost and whip it, it's still cruelty . . .

What will happen to all the animals when we don't eat them? said Mr. Smith.

We will be saturated by uneaten sausages, said Axel. What happens to all the poor women who don't get raped, what happens to . . .

The man who was paying looked up; he looked at Axel and then he looked at Mr. Smith. Then he started to look under the plates.

The bill please, Mr. Smith said to the waiter. They all left.

Axel takes a long time to escape from his speaking style, Lomas said. I think he takes longer than any other speaker. I remember once walking with him through the Park Lane garages and he stopped and said that this was to be his bathroom and that he had assigned various places in London for his private accommodation when the revolution came.

I remember the same sort of thing, Cafferty said. We went to Kenwood House a couple of weeks ago . . . he wanted to show me a painting by Dürer, which was there. . . .

Starting to fancy yourself, aren't you, said Freddie Kilennen.

No, said Cafferty. Anyhow we freewheeled down the path to the house . . . he called it Jewish overdrive for some reason, and when we got there he said that this was to be his private palace of delights, his sans souci. . . .

Strange, Lomas said. If you meet Axel in or around the park

and then listen to him on the platform there's no great change, is there? The gestures are the same: big, operatic. All the intonations, they're the same. I mean, the other speakers change on the platform: the expressions they made to you before they got up aren't the expressions they make to the crowd. They're borrowed from some image the speaker has built of himself in front of a crowd, with a few frames missing. Axel's the same on and off the platform . . . schizophrenic, with the two people he's divided into both exactly the same.

He said to me the other day, said Cafferty, that he got on a platform because somehow getting on a platform brought him a great deal of silence. It was easier to give a lecture than to involve himself in a kind of vociferous jungle . . .

You see, Lomas went on, his projected personality is with him when he does quite ordinary pallid things, like buying tea, buying newspapers, asking for the time . . . I think it is a relic.

A relic? what of? said Freddie Kilennen.

A relic of the old days of the park when it was a way of life: people slept there, people ate there and people made love there. In the park, before the war, there weren't any railings round the trees, you see, and the grass was very high, and there were lots of fat sheep loafing around, for cover. You could have a girl behind a tree in those days for half a crown. There was a sense of urgency in those days. When it rained people went into the end hall of Lyons and spoke there; it was the days of the hunger marches which used to end in the park under a welter of . . .

All right, all right, said Freddie Kilennen. Get to the point.

Well, there was no reason to behave differently on the platform from off, you were in the same position as the crowd, on or off. You weren't an object of curiosity. You were there from a challenge and response situation, a them and us situation. Axel is one of the last speakers to feel this. With the other speakers the challenge and response situation is in their own minds. . . .

Did he ever tell you he felt this way? said Freddie Kilennen.

No, Lomas said. He hasn't put it that way.

The platform manner wears off the further away he goes, Cafferty said. I remember going to Karl Marx's grave with him in Highgate cemetery, which he also said would serve some private function when London was allocated to him after the revolution. He made a few fabian calculations about the value of the marble on the grave and the lack of funds for medical research and then he changed the subject and started talking about the park in the old days. He was very relaxed, a different man.

Do you remember Sammy the Jew? Cafferty had said as they walked back to the cemetery gates from the grave.

Sammy the Jew? oh, yes . . . Sammy the Jew. You don't remember Sammy the Jew do you? His favourite phrase was: 'the baker bakes your bread, the miner digs your coal, the tailor makes your clothes. What do YOU do?' He used that. I got that off him. But don't get me wrong, a lot of speakers pinch my phrases . . . I myself am a dignified cripple. I am entirely uneducated . . . I heard somebody using that the other day, and that could only have come from me. When I hear them using my phrases I drop them . . . What's his name? that man with the platform on the grass, he even pinches my phrases. I'm not suggesting that he's not the possessor of a superabundant fund of wit of his own, but he does . . .

Oh, and then there was Frederick Law, the Jesuit, you remember him; and Ogilvie's girl friend, the blonde one. For years she just used to stand there staring at him. Sammy the Jew you know, he was VERY patriotic. He was a maniac. He used to like singing the arias from *La Bohème*, and we used to follow him down to Waterloo Bridge and he'd ask us to stand on the staircase, and stand and watch, and then he'd come down dressed as somebody very important . . . Henry the Fourth or something.

Then there was Major Viser, do you remember Major Viser? He was a very bitter white Zionist: 'I like the British, I like the British. I don't know whether I like them boiled or fried.' I got that off him . . . and then there was that other Sam of course. He was VERY nice . . . VERY nice. I sometimes still see him. He's grown a beard now. He used to have a very attractive north country accent. Very attractive personality. He used to say: 'The Lord loooves you . . . The Lord loooooves you,' and then he used to start reading his bible and get stuck, like this: '. . . and the Lord says . . . er . . . and the Lord says . . . er . . . THUS saith the Lord . . . THUS saith the Lord . . . er . . . It shall come to pass . . . er . . . SAITH THE LORD . . . er . . . yes, well anyway He LOOOOVES you.' And Aggie of course, dear Aggie. She once anointed me with a tin of boot polish. She didn't throw it at me. She meant it quite seriously. She hadn't got anything else handy . . . and do you remember Bloody Mary? she's dead now of course. Poor Bloody Mary . . . run over in Park Lane. Poor Bloody Mary, walking about with her blackboard: D-O-G equals G-O-D equals something . . . equals M-A-N, or the other way round . . . something. Poor Bloody Mary, she was very gone. She was very offensive too. She used to pull the hairs out of my legs when I was on the platform.

Axel is a driving instructor. He lives with his wife Gladys, his two daughters and his dog in a flat in Hornsey, which he uses as an office to run his driving school: The *Twenty Pound School of Motoring*. The idea behind it was that he contracted with the pupils to give them as many lessons as they needed to pass the Ministry of Transport driving test. It did not catch on. He was forced in the end to sell the contracts for as little as two pounds and then he found that his books were filled with people who had no chance of passing the test, but who still demanded an infinite amount of lessons from him on the strength of the contract, and they provided him with no income. So, he changed the system, but the name remains on the driving school car.

I also gave them their money back if they failed, Axel said. I don't know how I managed it, but I still couldn't get rid of the contracts. They don't believe you unless you overcharge them, and if you give them lessons for next to nothing, they want them for nothing.

At home Axel sits in his office waiting for telephone calls and for the next appointment. He draws his chair close to the table and his elbows on it, his hands clasped: one hand clutching the fist of the other, and his fingers flapping at the gaps between the knuckles; unclasping them to flick his teeth with his finger nail, and jumping up from time to time to put the gramophone back to the beginning of the *Song of the Steppes*.

Did you always have your own driving school? said Cafferty. No . . . no, I didn't. Before I started teaching people to drive, I used to work as a lorry driver, and I had a cab too, and before that I worked in a whisky distillery. It was scotch whisky, distilled and bottled in Scotland . . . just off Gardner's Corner, Aldgate East. Do you want another cup of tea? Gladys? Gladys? . . . Glad? another cup of tea. But I used to live in Hammersmith during the war. I was bombed out there actually . . . bombed out. I'll tell you about it . . . no reason why I shouldn't. One day (I never used to go into the shelters you see), then one day (he lowered his voice), I saw a very attractive woman going into the shelter with her bedding. When people used to use these surface shelters, they used to come in in the mornings or sometime, bring in their bedding and as it were, reserve the bunk; and I thought, you see, that she'd make a very nice friend. So, that day I decided that I would go into the shelter, and I rushed home and collected some bedding and reserved a bunk. That night I went into the shelter and there were about, I should think, eighty people (it was highly populated at the time), and I actually never saw that girl again. It was rather embarrassing. I mean you can't just pull away a blanket and say: Excuse me, are you that delightful little thing I saw trying to get into the shelter earlier today? so I walked up and down pretending to be fetching water, but I didn't see her, so I just thought I'd go to sleep instead, which I did.

The next day, when I came home, it wasn't. It was gone, the house. So, you see, if it wasn't for my wicked ways I wouldn't be here, or anywhere else.

No, said Cafferty.

I'll tell you another thing about that house. I used to house deserters there. I just met them in one place or another . . . at one time I had three. I had a British deserter and two American ones. I looked after them. You didn't bother to hide them, you just housed them. They used to go out at night because it was very safe then with the blackout. I was about sixteen then, I suppose.

Were you in work then? said Cafferty.

I've always been in work, said Axel. I had jobs navvying, driving and so on. I worked hard, you know. I was always punctual, punctilious and considerate. I only lost jobs because of personal incompatibility, and looking back now I must say that in all fairness I think that I withstood the intimate company of those people with remarkable courage and tenacity. I couldn't do it now. Jobs that I held for two or three months with unkind and unlovely and unloved and unlovable, ignorant dirty and unpleasant people . . . well, I couldn't do it now. Nowadays I'd just go. But in those days I used to think: well, a year, two years, so what? so I've been swallowing dust and dirt and bad company for a year or two? It doesn't matter. But nowadays I'm more conscious of the reality of our mortality. You see, we haven't got an eternity. Life is a limited thing. Very limited . . . and in fact, since then I worked in a mortuary too, and saw a lot of people die. Dead. Particularly with tuberculosis. . . .

What was your job in the mortuary? said Cafferty.

I was just a mortuary porter . . . ah, thank you Gladys. Tea?

Yes, said Cafferty.

I was just a mortuary porter. I had to go to various wards, pick up the bodies, put them on a trolley, wheel the trolley to the lift, and then go down the lift and wheel them about to the morgue, and then put the bodies onto a tray which was pushed into the fridge. I'd seen dead bodies before that, but not in such profusion. What shocked me more than anything else, I think, was how healthy the bodies looked. In fact, while I stayed there (I wasn't there an awfully long time), but while I was there, I should think all the bodies were under twenty five years of age. That shook me. And I had a very sudden and passionate religious phase at that time, and when the morgue was empty I used to take out recently dead people and kneel beside them and pray so that they'd revive, recover or something. I had an intense thing then. . . . I needn't tell you that my prayers remained unanswered. . . . I never wanted it for myself . . . I only wanted these people to live. I thought it was unspeakably sad . . . unspeakably sad. . . .

What are these internal injuries that you speak of? said Cafferty.

Hernia . . . double hernia. You see, before I was a driving instructor I was a truck driver, but I had to give it up because it involved loading and unloading and I couldn't stand up to the strain of it. So, the only thing to do was to look around for something else. There was no money in the house, there never is, and the only thing I was qualified to do was drive. I don't like being desk bound. I don't like being in commercial enterprises. I like being mobile. So, I went to an instructors' school and when I saw how easy it was, and that I had the temperament for it and the talent (people said of me that I was a dedicated teacher), I offered my services to various schools, who all thought very highly of me but grossly underpaid me, and last year, just over a year ago actually, I was discharged by the school for alleged anti-semitism . . . a lot of nonsense of course. It was very funny. actually, how it came about. My boss's name was Silverstein and he used to pay me seven pounds ten a week. That was my wage, and this involved working all the days of the week, all the hours of the day . . . there's an ash tray there . . . there's another one over there . . . and among other things I had to pick up a pupil in Hampstead.

One day, when I called for her, I noticed a Muzzuzzah there, that's a little container attached to the doors of Jewish households; we used to have one. It used to contain the first sentence of the ten commandments. I don't know how you spell it ... anyway you like, it's a hebrew word: M-U-Z-Z-U-Z ... anyhow some vowel, a few Z's you see ... and I saw this Muzzuzzah on the door post, and she was quite a nice girl apparently, and so naturally I said to her: I see this Muzzuzzah on your door (incidentally I had to collect her on Saturdays, the sabbath, Saturday afternoons actually), I said I've noticed a Muzzuzzah on your door, and she said yes. I said Oh, because I was surprised because I didn't think you were Jewish. I said this in the nicest possible way, and she immediately jumped to the defence of the Jewish people as if I had said something quite violent you see, and she pointed out to me that Jews were better than other people and that they were the chosen people; and when I asked her whether she kept the commandments, she became a little irritated and soon pointed out that she didn't comply with any of the rubrics of Judaism. But she thought that they were definitely superior, which I found rather revealing you see ...

They sacked you for that? said Cafferty.

Yes. The next time I saw her Silverstein had just given me the sack, or he implied that he would have to give me the sack because business wasn't very good. I forget the details. I had given him a year of jolly good service, and put up with a lot from him and his staff. I'd not only given tuition but helped in the workshops, collected spare parts and driven his wife and child about as a chauffeur. ...

Anyway, the next time I met this young girl, Axel went on, tipping his chair back, she caught me as it were, in a moment of indifference, to say the least, so that when she said something or other provocative: such as what do I think of the Jewish race, I used one of my superlatives, explaining of course that it was all meant in fun and that there wasn't any real difference between one race and another, and that a Jewish employer was just as unscrupulous towards his employee as a gentile one, and that the relationship between the Jewish master and servant was a master and servant relationship, and that one kind of master wasn't really to be preferred to another, and that when Jews found themselves in positions of authority they tended to abuse this authority, just as eskimoes, fuzzy wuzzies, thorough-bred teutonic Germans, or any other kind of sub species, and we left it at that.

The next time I had an appointment with her she didn't turn up at all, and I was called into the office and told that I was immediately dismissed because of anti-semitic utterances. So I just left it at that.

What did you do then? said Cafferty.

I found myself out of a job now, but with an awful lot of connections, you see. There were about thirty or forty people who swore by me, and didn't want to go to anybody else. As it happened I was rather fortunate because a colleague, another instructor with the same firm was a very poor, very bad instructor, and so consequently I was very popular. I had a very high percentage of success, far higher than most other instructors get, so that I'd be without a job for many months if I looked for another kind of occupation, but if I could go on with instructing right away, you see, then I could have a ready made job with a ready made income.

Well, it so happened at that time I knew someone who was prepared to lend me the necessary money to get a deposit on a car and to have the insurance and so on. Frank, his name was. I did it. It was all done within twenty four hours, and then away I went and I was a driving school. I took all their pupils away, and whenever I went over to their school I found their car idle. I enjoyed that very much, and since then there's been a steady flow of new people. Here's a list of people who've passed within the last three months: forty eight. There were fifty pupils who went in for the test and forty eight passed. That's good isn't it? that's good.

It doesn't satisfy me I suppose. I suppose it doesn't satisfy me, but it's one of those jobs which isn't any good in itself but it's so much better than any of the other jobs . . . wait a moment, there were two more, Hills and Flack . . . that's fifty out of fifty two, that's good . . . that's good. I've had some interesting people, mind you. Doctor Pilkington's son, he was one of my pupils, he passed with me. Then I had a racing driver, at least he's a racing driver now. . . .

Did you go and see him again? Lomas said.

That was a fortnight ago, Cafferty said. I saw him again yesterday. He was very different, very depressed. I think his daughter was in much worse health, the driving school was doing very badly and he was falling into debt. We went to see Frank, this man who put up the money for Axel to start his own driving school.

We will have to go and see Frank, Axel said. You'll find him very interesting, he takes invisible photographs of invisible people . . . we'll go in the car. It won't take long.

Frank works as a fireman in a West End cinema. Axel informed the commissionaire that he wanted to see Frank. The commissionaire disappeared and told them they would have to wait on his time until he was ready to see them.

Axel sat waiting on a bench in Soho Square eating black olives and cheese. He pointed to a house just round the corner:

I used to pick them up in Hampstead and take them there, to that house there, when I ran a cab, to play cards for money; then I'd stand about waiting for a sixpence tip and be pleased. I wouldn't do that now . . . they can stuff the sixpence up their muzzuzzahs.

He flicked the olive pips straight down on the ground with the tips of his fingers and then got up and arranged them into a circular pattern with the end of his boot. He sat back and stared at it:

And when I had Catholic pupils, I used to go with them into

church before the test, and kneel down and then I'd cross myself with them. It used to clear them. I become all things to all people . . . one of them saw me in the park once. I was being violently anti-catholic. Still . . .

Frank was ready to see them.

You must be very sympathetic, Axel said, because he talks about these invisible people all the time.

Frank was sitting in a room in Frith Street, staring at a picture of the sky at night filtering through prisms and changing into people wearing nineteenth century costumes. He was small, round, bald and friendly. He was pleased to see them.

Hello, hello hello, Axel, come in, come in. How's the driving school getting on?

This is Cafferty, said Axel.

Nice to meet you, said Frank, nice to meet you. Take a seat if you can. Well now, Axel, what have you been up to? I'm just about to bring out a pamphlet about the invisible people, you know. I've just finished writing the text of it. Would you like to see it?

Indeed, Axel said, and Frank took out a piece of yellow paper from his pocket.

It's in two parts, said Frank, the first part is called THE SPECTRUM AND POLARIZED LIGHT. . . .

Good, Axel said lighting his pipe.

'It has been discovered,' said Frank reading from the paper, 'that when polarized light is projected into the colours of the spectrum, it will bring into view the presence of invisible people and other worlds. If you are interested in these matters you are invited to try the following instructions: The phenomena is best observed in open spaces, such as public parks or similar places . . .'

Public parks? said Axel.

Yes, said Frank, anywhere that's open, why?

Nothing, nothing, said Axel. Carry on.

'The safest procedure is to be quite certain whether your path is clear in front of you,' Frank went on, 'because you must walk a few paces with your eyes closed. It is essential to hold the polariscope and prism near your eye and at the same time look front with a strong gaze, as you take your paces steadily forward. It is quite possible that you will not see anything at your first attempt or that you may feel sceptical, if not a little ridiculous. But success will come in the end . . .' that's the first part Axel, what do you think of it?

Very good, said Axel, very good indeed.

The room had once been a theatre dressing room, and Axel sat on the dressing table idly swivelling the wings of the mirror.

The second part is called THE CONSTRUCTION OF A POLARISCOPE, Frank said. I explained it all to you before, it's rather long Axel. . . .

Well, said Axel, I'm sure Cafferty would like to know how to construct the polariscope. Read on.

Frank lifted the yellow paper up to his face again and went on:

'The prisms used in these instruments are made from minerals, such as Tourmaline or Iceland Spar. The oblong prisms are ground to a special angle in the case of Tourmaline. But with Iceland Spar the polarization of light takes place inside the crystal itself. . . . I've put these minerals in capital letters. They give a strong field of polarization. . . . Then we have the glass plate polarizers and also half silvered mirrors which are employed for the polarization by reflection, when fixed at the correct angle. The easiest and cheapest of these are the glass plate polarizers, and there are no problems attached to the making of this useful instrument. The number of plates consist of less than a dozen in each block and they measure up to . . .'

Frank, Axel said, what I really wanted to talk to you . . .

'Up to five inches long,' Frank said. 'The polarization is secured when they are together. . . .' I've drawn it here, you see Axel? Here's a picture of it. It's very simple isn't it?

Yes, said Axel.

The first block is approximately twenty five degrees to any light source . . . well I'll skip that bit. It's about polarizing the light by extinguishing it, you see. If a torch light is used the filament will appear black you see. I've put it all in apostrophes we can skip that bit. . . .

Frank, said Axel, closing the wings of the mirror onto the face of the centre panel, look Frank, what I came to see you about was . . .

I'm just coming to the end, said Frank, if Mr. Cafferty is not bored.

No, said Cafferty.

This is what you are required to gaze into, Frank went on, using also the colours of the spectrum in the prism. These prisms are bought from opticians or from dealers in ex-government optical stock, telescopes and so on.

'When you try out these instructions it is important to know that the surrounding air, and the air in front of you, is your media, and its penetration is your quest . . .' block capitals for that: capital Q, capital U, capital E, capital S, capital T, and so on and so forth, well, that's it in fact, quest. . . . 'Look and see for yourself: invisible people that are dressed in old fashioned clothes, that walk along streets and highways as we do, ride in vehicles and live as we do ourselves: observe ships on the ocean, large ships and small craft. See small towns and big cities, with the rivers flowing through them, bridges that span them, and the busy movement of the railways, and the industrial activity that is going on there and everywhere. Then you may meet others who are trying to attract your attention to them by the same means. These people will call themselves spirituals. . . .' That's the end.

What do you think of it, Axel? Frank said stuffing back the piece of paper in his pocket, and looking carefully at Axel. It's going to cost a lot of money having this printed up . . . it'll set me back quite a bit, quite a bit.

Yes, Axel said carefully, yes I expect it will. Well, Frank, we mustn't keep you.

Thanks, said Cafferty. It was interesting.

Frank showed them out through the stage door, and pointed out a notice above it: THE WORLD'S GREATEST ARTISTES HAVE PASSED AND WILL PASS THROUGH THESE DOORS.

Yes, Axel said. Goodbye Frank.

Goodbye.

You know, said Axel as they left, if you have parasitic tumours and growths in your hair, you would wash them out, but if they're in your inside you do nothing; and by doing nothing you glamourize the situation. A friend of mine gave me a bed one night when I was driving a truck through Bristol and there were bugs everywhere. In the morning he said: Did you find a peaceful night? No, I said, there were bugs. Ah, he said, but they were all under the covers, weren't they. . . . Frank is rather like him.

He meant, Lomas said, that when Zarathustra comes down from the mountain he is sometimes forced to suffer fools gladly.

Open your mouth and hide behind it, said Freddie Kilennen.

$$*\qquad*\qquad*\qquad*\qquad*$$

The man who shot Kennedy did this because Kennedy was ultimately UNAPPROACHABLE! They ARE ultimately unapproachable, these people who speak in terms of DEATH and VIOLENCE! they can only be touched by DEATH or VIOLENCE! If somebody had shot Hitler in 1938, then he would have been replaced by Goering, but if somebody had bumped off Goering then he would have been replaced by Himmler, but if somebody had bumped off Himmler then he would have been replaced by Frick, but if somebody had bumped off Frick then he would have been replaced by Goebbels. . . .

THE POINT IS THAT WHILE THEY WOULD HAVE
BEEN REPLACING EACH OTHER THERE WOULD HAVE
BEEN NO WAR. . . .

You've no right to be saying that. Kennedy was murdered two
days ago, and you should pause to respect the dead. Get down!

If you can't speak to people, Axel went on, then you have to
shoot them, and that is all there is to it. That is what poor Mr.
Grunvald saw when he bumped off Von Blaht in 1938 on the
eighth of November. That is what the Croatian patriots saw
when they bumped off Crown Prince Ferdinand at Sarajevo in
nineteen fourteen. That is what Brutus saw when he . . .

Get down! get down you hairy bastard.

Spare no sympathy for Kennedy, my friends. He was an
opportunist as is the man who follows him and the man who
follows him. Assassination is an act of despair. It is sad. There is
no alternative. Anyone who's ever been in solitary confinement
as I have . . .

Get away!

Anyone who's ever been in solitary confinement as I have looks
up in his cell from time to time, for no reason whatever, except
that at least some judge or magistrate will know the despair and
bitterness that comes to a man hopelessly cut off from society.
You think they have only to push a bell button to put you there.
BUT THERE IS NO BELL, THERE ARE NO BELLS . . .
AND ASSASSINATION IS LIKE THAT. . . .

I think, said Lomas who was listening, that Axel is about to
join the ranks of the speakers where the challenge and response
situation is in their own minds.

Cafferty went to have a meal with Axel during the following
week, and after the meal Axel sat back waiting as usual for pupils
to ring up and engage him. He spoke slowly and spasmodically,
searching for the few soft bars in the *Song of the Steppes* to speak
against:

My mother was German, Axel said. My father was Russian
. . . they were both murdered. I don't know much about my
natural father, I called my step-father my father, you see. My
natural father was killed in the first war, but my step-father was
murdered when he went to complain about my mother being
locked up. It was in Berlin . . . it was during the war . . . on the
eleventh of July . . . I've seen people die violently who didn't even
know how to spell the . . .

The telephone rang.

Fitzroy two seven six one. . . . Batin? who lives where? I'm
sorry, I've never heard of him or her . . . I'm sorry, yes. Goodbye.
. . . My fathers were both in the German army. My natural father
was on the general staff in the Kaiser's army. My step-father was
in the ranks. . . .

They reported my mother you see, she was half Jewish. She
was reported to the authorities by a Jew for some trivial alleged
offence pertaining to food. Apparently he resented the fact that
she had been given more than her rations. . . . They called me
Mosaish, Mosaic. That's someone who's a quarter Jewish, they
worked it out very carefully. Mosaic, that was someone who was
all right racially, more or less, but . . . But, don't get this wrong,
from the point of view of anti-semitism, I never suffered. I
suffered far more in England both as a suspect German and a
suspect Jew.

But still, I came to England . . . here, I'll show you my passport,
you see: STATELESS underneath Complexion: fresh. I was
Polish you see, they've crossed it out and put Stateless. I was
Polish because my mother was on very good terms with the
Polish ambassador in Berlin and it was very difficult for German
subjects to move freely in Germany, so she had me registered as a
Polish citizen just like that. The Polish ambassador churned out
Polish nationality like bus tickets just to accommodate people,
especially people of Jewish origin, but I could never go back
there because the part of Poland which I was a national of, until

my citizenship dissolved, is deep in the Ukraine . . . so, I came to England.

The *Song of the Steppes* ended, and the record circulated. The needle transmitted the sound of deep, infected breath. Axel turned and gazed for several minutes through the metal framed windows at his spare little garden. Cafferty drank his tea. Axel turned back again:

I want to tell you something . . . do you ever have nightmares?

Not often, said Cafferty.

For twenty years I haven't slept without waking up with a nightmare.

What are they about? said Cafferty.

It's over twenty years now, over twenty years. Nightmares about prison. You see, my father was imprisoned in France for seven years, then he was imprisoned in Holland, then he was imprisoned in Germany by the Gestapo. He was imprisoned by the French for being in the German Army, and he was imprisoned by the Dutch for not having a passport issued to him by the Germans when he left Germany. They were very unreasonable in those days. . . .

When were you in prison? said Cafferty.

After the war, Axel said. I've had these nightmares ever since the war. They are nightmares about being in prison, about being separated from my family, about being frightened and helpless, about being locked up.

The official reason was contempt of court. I went into the wrong courtroom, I could hardly speak any English then, you see. I was summoned to appear on an aliens' charge, which was dropped or something, and I was only a young boy and they just grabbed hold of me, but I'd asked a police officer where I should be with all my papers. He caught hold of me, and he took me into a court where several old men were sitting round an improvised table or something. It was a makeshift court. It was the war, and two of them were nodding asleep, and one was filling his pipe or something; it was quite a jovial bunch. They just had me locked up. I didn't understand it, I suppose it was a contravention of the Aliens Act. I think it was failing to report a change of employment to the police within forty eight hours.

I've never been in prison under conviction, always on remand. But before that I was locked up for being an orphan, in need of care and attention. That was because I'd attempted to limit the perverse powers over the children in one of these establishments, that this devoted swine of a tyrant, this professional state paid guardian who was responsible for me, exercised. He made life miserable for me. Anyway, I was locked up for organizing a union. It was a union for orphans. We decided to band together and go to the police and complain against the indecencies that our guardian practised against us. If we went together, they'd listen to us, we thought, and I made a little speech at an opportune time, but one of them had a girl friend and she wrote this down in her diary. The guardian went through the girl's drawers, in more senses than one, read the diary and had me sent to the police in London as being in need of care and attention, and I was locked up in a remand home with other kids whose parents had been killed in air raids. They were orphans. They were locked up because they were orphans.

But I don't get nightmares from that. I get nightmares from the time I was in Wormwood Scrubs during the air raids, for the aliens' offence. I was shocked by it. I WAS shocked . . . the dirt . . . the stench . . . I won't forget it. After the war I could have been naturalized for nothing. I could have had all the advantages of British naturalization by signing a form, and without paying a penny. It would have been so easy, but I didn't want it. It has advantages. They can't call you up and they can't take away your citizenship as a punishment, and the best one is that you can't be deported anywhere. Where can you send a stateless man? Where? I can't HAVE the nationality of any race . . . what race am I? Ukrainian? Polish? German? Jewish?

Axel?

Yes? what is it?

Don't forget you've got Mr. Gapps.

No, all right. Thank you Gladys . . . but I suppose, I suppose, if I was forced back onto one of them, it would be German. My home is the British sector of Berlin, but they won't LET me go home. They think I'm a rabble rouser . . . The Jews were Germans, the Jews WERE Germans, that's why they couldn't stand them. Let me tell you what we Germans have done for you. We gave you your Royal family, we gave you your language, we have given you MUSIC, we have given you BEETHOVEN, BACH, SCHUBERT. . . .

He got off his chair, dragged it into the middle of the room and stood on it:

. . . and SCHUMANN, and MOZART, GLUCK and MAHLER, and then when you got sick of conservatism we gave you REVOLUTIONARIES, MARX and FRIEDRICH ENGELS. . . . We gave you HEGEL, and I was going to say we gave you KANT, but I can never remember how to pronounce it. We gave you TOLSTOY! We gave you TCHAIKOVSKY . . . we populated RUSSIA . . . we're ALL OVER the world . . . in AMERICA . . . and then some of them became Jewish and went to Israel, and England is a VERITABLE GARDEN where Germans go to when they're tired of work . . . wonderful, BEAUTIFUL people. They're BEAUTIFUL . . . they were tormented by such a superabundance of love that they went on and on psychoanalysing themselves on every altar but their own. And LOOK what you've created with your market gardening in Africa. You butchered all the natives, so that when the Negroes come to England, they start beating ME up as if I were a bloody Anglo Saxon . . . I'm ALWAYS willing to be deported to my home town in Germany which is BEAUTIFUL and we KNOW when the sun shines and KNOW when the snow will fall, AND BEAUTIFUL GERMAN CHILDREN WILL SING BEAUTI-

FUL GERMAN SONGS ONCE THEY HAVE DISPOSED
OF YOUR BEAUTIFUL ANGLO SAXON TROUBLES
WHICH YOU HAVE IMPOSED ON THE BEAUTIFUL
GERMAN LAND. . . .

Axel caught a gesticulating hand in the light flex. The lamp
crashed to the floor. The dog started to bark.

Axel? is anything the matter?

No, no nothing at all . . . nothing, Gladys.

Well remember Mr. Gapps . . .

Yes, yes Mr. Gapps . . . yes. Where do you want to get to
Cafferty?

Oh, the tube station will do.

Right, Axel said, we'll get Mr. Gapps to drive you there. Sit
in the back and pretend you're a pupil.

They went up to the garage on Muswell Hill where Axel keeps
the driving school car. He opened up the bonnet and took out a
large theatre lamp from it, wound up the flex and hung it on the
wall:

My mother bought this before the war, said Axel, she used to
focus it on me when we entertained ourselves in the evenings.
I used to give long recitations from the German satirical poets.

They went to fetch Mr. Gapps, and waited in the car until he
came out:

You know, Axel said, I've lost a fantastic amount of money
through menstruation. If my pupils are menstruating that means
that they don't turn up, and if they're not menstruating, then
they're worried that they're late and they're unteachable. All
women are ninety five per cent womb and five per cent gossip
. . . but men, you see, men think that women are just negative
men. They're not. They have lost me a fortune. But Mr. Gapps is
a model pupil . . . ah, Mr. Gapps, how are you today?

Very well thank you, said Mr. Gapps edging into the driving
seat.

Now, Mr. Gapps, we've got to get you past the test haven't we. Don't wipe the windscreen with your hands, Mr. Gapps. Use the demister. Now, ignition, that's it. Start up, will you. Remember your lights, is this a well lit street? could you read a newspaper in the car? No, then put on your lights. Change up, off with the gas on with the clutch, change gear, on with the gas, off with the clutch. That's right, Mr. Gapps, keep your hands at ten to two on the steering wheel. Now you see Mr. Gapps if you hadn't got your lights on, you'd have knocked down that piece of animated cosmetics crossing over there by the corner . . . Would you mind closing the window Mr. Gapps, in consideration of the weather? thank you . . . You're interested in football aren't you Mr. Gapps? So is Mr. Cafferty here. Do you remember how the football cup, the gold cup, or whatever it was, got stolen once under the noses of the detectives?

The F.A. cup was stolen once, yes, said Mr. Gapps.

Well, they took that cup to the place where I worked and my employer melted it down.

Charming, said Mr. Gapps.

Clerkenwell it was, Axel went on, it was a gold and silver foundry and I spent eighteen months slogging away there. He paid me a pound a week, can you believe that Mr. Gapps? I used to unlock the place at eight in the morning and lock it up again at nine at night, and work solidly all day for a pound a week which all went to my guardian, and I got a threepenny allowance each day for my bus fares to work and back. So I used to get up early, walk to work and save the threepence. . . . I put it in a little mannikin cigar tube, Cafferty, in case my parents were still alive. I thought I'd save up for them for after the war . . . Signal, always signal Mr. Gapps. You don't mind the wireless, do you Mr. Gapps?

Axel turned it on, folded his arms tightly and hunched forward with his elbows on his knees:

Conservative majority, said Axel after a bit, Conservative

majority. . . . Rents will go up by about fifty per cent, thus turning about three million people out of house and home. These three million people will be encouraged to earn extra money by working for the government and will be employed building bigger prisons. As soon as they've completed building them they'll be out of work. When they're out of work they'll no longer be able to pay the inflated rents, and so they'll go to the prisons they've just been constructing, and there they'll work for the state and that's how the balance of employment and unemployment is kept level in the British state economy. . . . And then you have debates in Parliament as to whether mid-week football is a good thing, or whether it keeps people away from the factories, and nobody minds about mid-week Wimbledon tennis . . .

That is a fact in every way, Mr. Gapps said.

Yes . . . slow down here, very gently, very gently. You're coming to the lights. You remember what to do, don't you Mr. Gapps? Don't chop and change lanes, Mr. Gapps. In a situation like that, just take a quick look over your shoulder to make sure that it's safe to come out . . .

This is the tube station Axel, Cafferty said.

Yes, said Axel. Stop here for a moment will you Mr. Gapps?

Mr. Gapps sat in the car with his hands at ten to two on the steering wheel, fingering the ignition key from time to time and then shaking his hand. The key had become very hot as the celanoid was broken. Axel stood on the pavement and closed the side door.

I wanted to tell you something else about the dreams, Cafferty. I had a terrible dream, a terrible dream. It keeps coming back to me, it came back just then. I couldn't get it out of my mind.

What was it? said Cafferty.

Well, don't laugh at it. You won't laugh at it, will you? But I dreamt I was in a Tunnel of Love, like they have in fairgrounds. You know, you have two wheeled carriages that trundle past tawdry eroticisms on runnels . . . and there was a heckler in the park, he doesn't heckle my meetings much, but sometimes. I had a terrific fight with him. But I ENJOYED it you see . . . there was a huge abattoir of blood. I enjoyed the violence, and as I came out of the tunnel parts of his face were there, held up by eleven hundred of his supporters . . . and I went on fighting it, and I ENJOYED the violence. That was what troubled me. I know I have vast wastes of tormented aggression, but in real life when I see a blind man I get STINGING pains in my eyes . . . and a lame one a sympathetic . . . all right, all right, Mr. Gapps. I just thought I'd tell him something you see, he's taking the test next week.

THE SINGING WOMAN: Mister Speaker . . .
AXEL: How did you know my name?
THE SINGING WOMAN: I can tell by your eyes.
AXEL: I bet you tell that to all the speakers . . .
THE SINGING WOMAN: Why don't you cut off your beard?
AXEL: Ah fair one . . . Madden me no longer, but utter the words that will ever see thy happiness. Goodbye. Someone, someone pour her back into the bottle . . . WHY DON'T YOU GO AND PLAY WITH THE TRAFFIC? Go and have an accident, and adjust the statistics to save somebody DECENT. . . . YOU are a BORE, you are a waster of my time and a waster of my breath. You are a waste of food, you are a waste of money, you are a waste of light. You are a waste of LOVE . . . you are a waste of pavement.

    You won't take a RISK. NONE of you will take a PHYSICAL RISK. When you heard a few weeks ago that someone had been shot for money, someone had taken a PHYSICAL RISK, you were shocked because you're used to thinking that all thieving and robbing and murdering should be conducted on little pieces of paper with free flowing ball point pens. Christine Keeler took a physical risk. She went to bed with a Conservative. And she also took tremendous emotional risk, because she must have been shocked when she discovered that a Conservative of the upper airs was actually heterosexual, and had something to offer her, better than a picture of his manservant. YOU would never have taken that risk.

Ladies and gentlemen, look, will you, at this graceful champion of British womanhood. She's the only woman in Hyde Park who's got a thicker moustache than I have. But ladies, God made her more perverse, God made this unhappy bundle of misconceived protoplasm. GOD MADE HER. God made her to make all you others feel more beautiful. Her mother should have kept a cork in her heart. This lady was not born, she was caught prematurely in a turnstile. BUT WE HAVE TO HAVE THIS KIND OF THING . . . We have to have these irritants so that we'll scratch ourselves. That bundle of perambulating protoplasm that is that stench over there . . . this kind of thing reminds us that we should be as careful of our seed as we are with our toothpaste. You are a haphazard darling little mish mash. You're something that we only whisper about and go visiting occasionally when we've got tuppence halfpenny to spend . . . DON'T YOU DESERVE TO DIE? don't you deserve to be TICKLED to death? and then the police will come and take you away with all the paraphernalia of heroism . . . a notebook and pencil.

That was unusually vicious, said Lomas who had been listening, what was the reason for that?

The driving school has been doing very badly, said Cafferty. Axel is fast falling into debt, I think there's some ratio between the state of the driving school and his family and the amount of abuse he directs at people in the park. Sunday is also the most profitable time to give driving lessons, and he said to me this afternoon before he got onto the platform: They are taking my money, my wife's money, my children's money. They swell my debts . . . and they are taking my life blood. The life of a speaker is very short.

Why doesn't he give it up then? Lomas said.

I don't know, said Cafferty.

Lomas and Cafferty left the park and came back several hours later. Axel was still speaking by the old refreshment stall and there were about ten people left. Two or three gazed fixedly at him, the rest had drawn their collars up and lowered their heads, and cigarette smoke lazed up from the damp pocket they had made to warm their faces, or they threaded and re-threaded the fringe of the meeting, looking nervously for other threads to follow:

Somehow the God which made man unheroic, Axel was saying, created in me an intense desire to explain. Not to mitigate, nor to acquit, nor to apologize, but merely to explain why we are doomed. It is after all nothing more than an act of confession. When an animal, any species of animal contradicts those forces in itself which had in the past made survival possible, then it is doomed to perish. There is no animal in nature today as helpless as we are. An animal feeds itself, selects its mate itself, builds its own home, protects its own home, struggles, fights and if he loses he is vanquished. He dies. He perishes. The audience is not embarrassed.

Now I have almost exhausted my repertoire and bitterness, and I invite you to hate me until next week. You will go away no doubt and say that mine is a minority opinion, and mine is the voice of one crying in the wilderness. But I want to remind you of the words of a philosopher who said that a man who stands with God, stands with the majority. If I speak the truth and all men around me are liars then I am comforted nevertheless by the glow, the warmth and the life and the energy, which my truth gives me. It was the Nazarene who taught me . . . by their fruits shall ye know them. I do not mind being in a minority. The beauty queen of the world is in a minority. Being in a majority makes a man weak. He is comforted by the stinking warmth of his companions. Goodnight.

He got down, picked up the stepladder, walked through the meeting and hashed up the delicate, spindled smoke.

If you tear out the pages of your Portable Nietzsche, you can make it more portable, Lomas said, and went back to Kilburn.

*   *   *   *   *

Axel and Cafferty were sitting in the pub opposite Bernard Shaw's house. Some men came in from shooting, with dogs and game and knickerbockers, and sat down with their lunch baskets and pink gins. Axel got up and went to the bar:

I want some crisps, he said. I do not want the kind which are obscenely saturated in animal fat . . .

The heads turned a little.

I want the cheese and onion flavoured crisps.

He sat down by the fire again, and started talking softly:

You know something? when I get off a platform, I suppose I feel like a woman who's just had a baby. I feel that it's done. The thing is over. It's slipped through now, it's out. Right? I think . . .

That is given as an explanation for several things, Cafferty said.

Yes, but listen, listen . . . I think that if I didn't speak I should be a very violent man. You see, during the week when things happen to me which would make other men feel very violent, I console myself with the knowledge that in a few days' time I shall be able to speak.

But the people responsible won't be there, Cafferty said.

I know they won't be there. I HOPE they won't be there, and I wouldn't want any of my friends or enemies to be there. You see, there are two things that I do when I'm on the platform. First of all I'm making friends: I'm giving people the reassurance that they're not alone in their dilemma, in their despair . . . And this . . . I must confess this: I have never got onto the platform without the feeling that I was actually practising, rehearsing for something else to come, something bigger one day. I think a lot of people spend years and years rehearsing and then they die before the play is ever put on. But it's still necessary to rehearse. I rehearse. . . . I rehearse . . . it's like getting on a stage and the people standing round you, they're the mock audience. You know when you have a stage rehearsal, there are usually some people about, the caretaker's little sister . . . all sorts of people, they're all sitting around, and they're not really supposed to be there, but the actors have to have them there. That's a paradox . . . that's nice. And I think that all the time, this is my apprenticeship, you see. I'm not an old man, you see. If I got over my financial difficulties and I'm not run over by a bus, the chances are that I may last another few years. . . .

He got up to buy some more drink.

Did you notice that I always say: run over by a bus?

No, said Cafferty.

You see, lorry has r's. That's the only letter I can't pronounce in any language. . . . I try, I try, but the word keeps flopping, and I'll tell you something else . . . when I was a small boy I stuttered a lot, you see. I had a stammer and I used to stand in front of a mirror to overcome that, and that, I think, I don't know for certain, but I think it was that which started me speaking. It was a challenge to me when I was young to speak aloud. I tried, and you know it's marvellous if you try an experiment with yourself and it clicks . . . marvellous . . . marvellous. . . .

*   *   *   *   *

Have you seen Axel? Freddie Killennen said in the *New Inn* a few weeks later. He hasn't been up the park for some time.

No, Cafferty said. His hernia's troubling him very much, and the driving school . . .

The driving school?

Well, that's what he does during the week, he has a driving school. I think it's doing very badly as he was in hospital for a bit.

I've seen him, Lomas said. He was up for a bit this afternoon, in very low spirits, wandering round the park abstractedly and then he stood on a milk crate from the stall. I didn't listen.

Some time later Axel came into the *New Inn* and began to talk of suicide as a means to balance the profit and loss, and of his boredom and his tiredness:

. . . and I don't want to be dictated to by pupils any more, he said to Cafferty. One of them, the day he was taking the test. . . . I had no money for petrol so I asked him if I could borrow some. Well . . . well, he felt himself like they do, and he said he hadn't got any on him. So, I asked him whether there was anybody in the house who could lend him some. No, he said. Well, I said, do you have a bank? Yes, he said. Well, where is it? It's in Finchley. So I drove him there, giving him a lesson on the way . . . practice in hill starts and so on, and dropped him at his bank . . . I said to him: I'll wait for you here, and do you know what he said? He said: I bet you will . . . I bet you will. So I shouted at him through the window: In that case I will unburden your mind of another certainty. I won't. I drove off.

Axel drank some more, listened half heartedly to Lomas who was talking about his old Syndicalist platform before the war, and then got up and drove back to his flat in Hornsey on his motor cycle.

I've heard him speak like that before, Lomas said when he had gone.

I haven't, said Freddie Killennen.

You never listen, said Lomas. But you see, while you were at the bar, Cafferty, he turned to me and he said that he'd thought of a new name for his struggle. He was going to have a notice with COMBAT NINETEEN SIXTY FOUR, on the front of his platform, and he told me that it would embody all his schemes, and all the things that he calls his scars on sorrow.

What if it fails? Cafferty said.

Why, then it will be called COMBAT NINETEEN SIXTY FIVE. He told me that himself.

*Don't you call me MISTER Webster. You've
got nothing on me.*

Webster

THE NATURAL LAW RELIGION. Speaker: WEBSTER.

Webster's is the tallest platform in the park. It is clean and
freshly painted in green gloss so that the chalk writing of old
creeds on the board in front will rub off easily.

He speaks from it under the gas lamp beyond the bull ring at
the verge of the grass; his features lit up, when the gas lamp is lit
above him, into a hard knot of gestured flesh which loosens to
pour out abuse. Dirty red hair hangs over his forehead; his tight
pupils flick about for targets in the crowd.

He stands in the same position for several hours, gripping the
top of the board with his white, freckled hands, hanging over it
and using his head as a pointing hand. Occasionally he descends
two or three steps when there are Irish or Muslim hecklers in the
crowd.

My name is Webster, Webster is saying. It had its origins with
spider. One who spins, you know. And I am quite a subtle
spinner. I am no priest: in fact, as soon as I see a priest, I turn the
other way. For, where you find a priest, there you find a professional scoundrel who lives on superstition, and who tries to

blackmail you into a hangover called heaven. Webster has no creed. I believe in nothing except the reality with which I am confronted, understanding it and dealing with it in terms of MY personality. Webster doesn't mind people disagreeing with him. It would be almost impossible to EXPECT them to agree with him. They would have to be as intelligent as him. Webster doesn't mind if somebody's a Christian. Webster's answer is: let the dead bury the dead. Webster's not concerned with your dying, as far as Webster's concerned you haven't even most of you, begun to live yet. Webster doesn't mind hecklers. Webster doesn't mind interrupters. And if you score a point off Webster, I'll be the first to laugh, so I can't be here to save you. Webster's not a communist. In Russia they force you to eat if you're a member of the working class, and Webster doesn't want to go to China. In Red China all the women wear overalls and carry stretchers. Webster's not a . . .

What could you get off him? said Cafferty to Lomas. They were listening in the crowd.

He's got the loudest cockney voice in the park, said Lomas turning away. You can hear Webster's voice before anyone else's, whatever gate you come in, and even if he's standing right over here in the open . . . What can you get off him? I don't know. He's got a tall platform . . . that's a help, and also some of the speakers are paid to hold meetings on very low platforms under the trees by the queers. They can use a crowd like that to satisfy their clumsy lust. Webster's platform is above suspicion. What can you get off him? listen on . . .

A man who speaks for the Protestant Truth Society had pushed his way to the front, and had started heckling:

Your mind's in a mental cemetery, Webster was saying, that's why you've got peace of mind. Do you know what thinking means? thinking means to STRIVE. Thinking means to SUFFER. Nothing was ever CREATED without suffering and you come round here telling me you've got peace. You mental eunuch . . .

who wants peace? I WANT WAR. WAR IS TO MAN WHAT CHILDBIRTH IS TO WOMAN. . . .

That war will destroy you . . . the heckler said.

OH! 'that war will destroy me' . . . LOOK I SHALL DIE ONE DAY. . . .

And face judgment, the heckler said.

FACE JUDGMENT! You tell me one person who came back after they were dead and produced evidence of judgment.

We've got God's word for that. . . .

NOW LISTEN TO HIM! He's got God's word for it and God is almighty. Every time he opens his bible he reads TRANSLATED and REVISED . . . in other words CORRECTED . . . according to James the First. So, in other words, James the First knows more than God does. Why do you come here with this RUBBISH? The Protestants have got a bible . . . and what ARE you Protestants? the very word Protestants suggests that you came from the Catholic church. All you are, you're Catholic heretics . . .

I'm a Christian, the heckler said.

You're a CHRISTIAN thank God Christ wasn't. Christian was a greek word, and Christ never spoke Greek . . . and even the greatest Christian scholars are agreed that God had nothing to do with the bible. What do you think God is? a bookmaker touting for the British and Foreign Bible Society? Don't come here bothering Webster with your rubbish. If you want to go to heaven GO there. You go and worry about judgment day. As for me, I'm pleading guilty . . . THIS INVERTED BOWL WE CALL THE SKY, WHEREUNTO LIVING PROOF WE LIVE AND DIE . . . THEN RAISE NOT YOUR HANDS TO IT FOR HELP. IT IMPOTENTLY MOVES AS YOU OR I. . . . YOUR LOVE OF VIRTUE! YOUR TALK ABOUT HEAVEN! . . . it's a psychological factor showing that you HAVEN'T got any peace. There's FEAR inside of you, and it's that FEAR inside of you that sends you on your knees worrying about what's going to happen to you after you're dead. What have YOU ever done that you could be punished for? START LIVING . . . Webster will be punished. If they punish me after I'm dead, I'll get a life sentence . . .

What can you get off Webster? said Lomas. Well, he's got a crowd of two or three hundred, I should think; and he'll keep most of them here for about three hours. But that type of heckler . . . he can fade them out as soon as winking. I don't know why he bothers. But you wait . . .

Lomas pointed out two women who had moved in behind Webster's platform: Cathleen the Hooligan, tall and dreamy, and The Singing Woman, who sings old hits from Collins's Music Hall when she is not heckling, and spins round in the middle of a crowd hitting them with her handbag when their enthusiasm wanes. Her real name is Doris.

They can ask questions which linger a bit, Lomas said. Listen on.

. . . and if I were you I'd put your head in the sand too, Webster was saying, because you're not really photographic . . . well, photogenic, pornographic . . . that's not the word at all. I am the inheritor of Shakespeare's language. It is a language which is interpreted in terms of the personality of the speaker . . .

You was anti-Jewish, wasn't you Webster, Doris said.

There was a pause. Webster looked down at Doris, then turned to the crowd:

Yes . . . yes, I was anti-Jewish. But I want to say this to you, if I was a jew and remembered the things that Webster has said and done, I would be against Webster. The fact is that I have not changed once; I have changed many times and I'll go on changing. Change means growth. I've been a communist. I was brought up a Christian, but I wouldn't go to heaven now, not if you paid me. If they rob you up there the same way as they rob you here, you wouldn't stand a chance. I'm thoroughly ashamed I was ever anti-Jewish.

Well, you have to say that, don't you. Doris said.

I don't mind if a Jew IS anti-Webster, Webster went on, ignoring her. Because communism grows out of social injustice, communism grows out of poverty, but fascism is a DISEASE. The Jews are now paying me five hundred pounds a week because I'm the best speaker they're ever likely to have. . . .

Can you prove it? Doris said.

I don't have to, said Webster. They'll all believe it.

Then can we have our money back?

No. You're not Jewish. Suppose Webster IS being paid?

I believe you are . . . a little bit.

I'll give this platform to anyone who can prove that Webster is being paid. So, if you know who's paying me, come up here and tell them.

You're getting something, Doris said. It comes by post.

Suppose I AM being paid? YOU'RE not concerned who pays me. YOU'RE concerned with what I say and your concern is to think about what I say, analyse what I say and then see if there's any truth in it. The question whether I'm being paid has nothing to do with the essential. . . .

Truth is like as long as long, isn't it, said Doris.

I'm SICK and TIRED of people saying I'M PAID. One week people come and say: Webster is being paid by Nasser . . . the next week they say: Webster is being paid by Ben Gurion . . . I'm not being paid by EITHER, but I wish those two would come together, it'd make a new perversion. And the week after that they say: Webster is being paid by the bloody pope. . . . I AM NOT BEING PAID.

HOW MANY WOMEN HAVE YOU GOT ON THE STREETS, WEBSTER? Freddie Kilennen shouted from the back.

Why is it that you must introduce your business affairs into the park? I assure you Webster is very different from you. You may have your women on the street, Webster has his in bed.

Lomas caught Freddie Kilennen's eye and they went over to Lyons:

He changed the subject, Lomas said.

It was changed for him, said Freddie Kilennen.

No, no, said Lomas. It's his old trick. He knows that his source of income is one of the most controversial things in the park, and he's only got to mention it, and then the subject is changed . . .

Well anyway, said Freddie Kilennen. He makes no secret of it, and it wasn't political. It was all to do with his marrying some German Jewish girl in Paris before the war to get her out of being returned to Germany, and he got cheesed off with her . . .

He used to supply books to Mosley in prison, Lomas said.

Did he dear? Oh, I didn't know about that.

Oh yes, Lomas said. When I first remember him he was speaking on the Irish platform, at the beginning of the phoney war, and working as an intelligence officer in the I.R.A. with an old crony of his in the park: Frank Corrigan, who was born in the same street as he was: Greyhound Road, Fulham. They locked him up under section 18A of the Defence of the Realm Act . . . that section was for aliens. 18C was for the others. They classed him as an alien because he had an Irish mother, and Frank Corrigan, they deported him, 'back' to a country he'd never been to.

Then when Webster came out, he took up with all this anti-semitics, opened up a fascist bookshop in Southampton Row and got the old Duke of Bedford to put up some money in it. Then the bookshop moved to Torquay, and Webster used to go off to Bristol and speak on the Downs. They used to supply Mosley and his henchmen with all their fascist literature while they were all in prison under 18C in the war, but then Webster switched, made a radical change in Mosley's reading list, and came back to London to speak for the I.R.A.

Webster and I are bitter enemies because of it, Cafferty, Lomas went on. He was a good speaker up until then, and I don't believe it had anything to do with his wife. He's also got some cock and bull story about how people, eastern european refugees, used to come into the park, when he was on the Trotskyist platform, and heckle him. They used to say that Trotsky was a mad fascist dog, and therefore Webster was a mad fascist bitch, and that turned him against the Jews. He's just vicious, that's all. Just vicious, and he makes capital out of the fact that he was connected with the blackshirts, because he knows it'll keep an audience.

Cafferty stayed on in the park listening in Webster's crowd. Cathleen the Hooligan and Doris had left, but the crowd had taken up the question and Webster was still explaining his anti-semitism:

The only mistake I've ever made, Webster was saying, and the only thing I'll ever despise myself for, is that I once became, at the beginning of the war, anti-Jewish. Believe me, I stand and I tell you this because I try to get rid of the guilt of it, that if there's anything I despise, if there's anything I loathe, it's those people who are anti-Jewish, because there you'll find the worst kind of reactionary. Where you find somebody who's anti-Jewish, there you'll find those who are the greatest enemies of mankind. Every damn dictator, every damn criminal, throughout the ages when he wanted something to hate when he wanted a whipping boy, he turned towards the Jews. I'm not against those little boys selling *Action*, I'm sorry for them, but I'm against their leader, coming down here in his dirty shirt telling us to put Britain first. I'm not against the German people, but I would be against the criminal Hitler. I'm not against the Italians but I'm against Mussolini and his adulteration of ice-cream. I'm against these kind of things.

All the other mistakes I've ever made have been a process of growing up. Anybody in history that I find was anti-Jewish was either an idiot or a scoundrel, and you know that I'm not an idiot. I was anti-Jewish because I was young, very emotionally involved and at that time I knew nothing about Freud and the subconscious power of sex. Now I know it all. I spend half my time in bed dreaming about politics. . . .

A man at the back started shouting obscenities. Half way through he seemed to be saying that he'd seen Webster distributing anti-Jewish pamphlets in the park last week. Webster pointed at him:

Any policeman could knock you off for that word alone.

I was knocked off this morning, the man said.

You were knocked off this morning? You've been knocked off all your life. Shutup . . . SHUTUP . . . SHUTUP . . .

Webster faced his crowd again:

He's a heckler. He always comes to my meetings. Last week HE was distributing anti-Jewish pamphlets . . . He behaves like a goat, he talks like a goat and he calls me anti-anti. And tonight he'll be blind drunk and singing 'There's a welcome in the back woods' . . . AND WHAT ARE YOU ENGLISH? you're all living on the H.P. and in the so-called affluent society and most of you are dead from the neck up . . . VOTE LABOUR. What's the sense in that? if you've got money, vote for the money. What's the use of voting for those who've got nothing? Vote for the man who's going to give something away, if he's got it; and if he hasn't got it, he's going to take it. I'd only join the Labour Party if they made me a lord . . . a landlord. Look at it. All your landlords, they're Greeks, Pakistanis, Jews, Poles, Italians, Blacks, and Indians . . . AND WHY SHOULDN'T THEY BE? If you English are so stupid . . . BOYS OF THE BULLDOG BREED! . . . you couldn't run a whelk stall. FORGET THIS RUBBISH OF RACE . . . if a cat is born in an orange box, is it a cat or an orange? They believe that Jesus was a fascist. They believe that Jesus had blonde hair and blue eyes. This is RUBBISH. You can do anything with science now. You can force black out and force white in; and if we can force black out and white in, why can't we force white out and black in? We could solve the problem by all of us becoming black men. And what's wrong with becoming a black man? a black man can do things in a black room that a white man can't . . .

What about brown men? said a brown man.

I never said brown men. Brown men are illuminated in black rooms. But I don't know . . . being ENGLISH . . . it's quite a NICE way of being a human being. There was an Irishman once who made a joke . . . he made a joke. The policeman came up to him and said: Why did you kick that Jew? the Irishman said: He killed God. The policeman said: Yes, but that was over two thousand years ago. The Irishman said I know, but I've only just heard about it. . . .

Cafferty left and went across to join Lomas in Lyons.

You make too much of it dear, Freddie Kilennen was saying, bringing back the teas from the counter. You make too much of the anti-semitism.

No one in the park would take that view, said Lomas. They have him for everything. They have him for deserting the communists, they have him for deserting the fascists, they have him for deserting the muslims, they have him for deserting the I.R.A., and they even have him for deserting the Salvation Army, he was in that too. I mean, he can come back at them, but he's picked up too many of them now. What's the time?

Cafferty looked at the clock.

You go back into the park when you've finished your tea. The Irish will be having a go at him then. I'll join you later.

They walked back through the echoing subway to avoid the traffic. The light was fading in the park, the gas lamp above Webster's head had been turned on, and his crowd had drawn closer together. The Irish meeting a few pitches away had ended and they were rolling up a green raffia fruit-barrow mat, that they'd had on the ground beneath the platform decorated with jampots of water full of flowers, and a cross at the head of it, reading HERE LIES WOLFE TONE. It had been the anniversary of his death. A few of those who had attended the meeting, squeezed their way into Webster's crowd: and formed a knot at the foot of his platform. Webster got down a couple of steps while he was speaking:

You bloody liar, Webster.

If I have told an untruth on this platform I publicly ask forgiveness, said Webster spreading out his arms. MEA CULPA . . . MEA CULPA . . . MEA CULPA . . . all Irishmen are artists because they are strangers to the truth. But THESE poor little Irishmen, they weren't even born when I was speaking under the orange, white and green in the park. I WAS BORN UNDER THE IRISH FLAG BROTHER BEFORE YOUR FATHER EVEN THOUGHT OF AMUSING HIMSELF. . . . Don't you come round here threatening me, because Webster was never afraid of violence from you, you son of the Gail, or anyone else. Webster lives in London. Webster walks round London. What have you got more than the corner boy violence of someone who says: Webster, don't you knock the Irish or I'll knock you? GET OUT . . . I will give this platform to any one of them if they can recite the 1916 Proclamation. . . . ALL RIGHT THEN I'LL DO IT FOR YOU . . . Irish men and Irish women, in the name of God and the past generations through which our country receives our old traditions and nationhood, Ireland. . . . THEY DON'T WANT IT EVEN! What could this rubbish tell you about Michael Davin? what could they tell you about Lorla? what could they tell you about Wolfe Tone or Cave Hill? what could they tell you about FitzGerald? what would they know about Ireland? All they know about Ireland is that they were born there and got out of it. And what about Patrick Pearce who wrote the poem: Since the wise men have not spoken, I speak who am only a fool? Patrick Pearce was shot in 1916, along with James Connolly, Liam Merrows, and Joe McElvy . . . all of them shot in twenty-two in the Four Courts, so that this rubbish can come here to spit out the name of Ireland. . . . I LOVE Ireland

and I want FREEDOM for Ireland, but God save Ireland from rubbish like you. Go back on the immigrant ship . . .

Shut your mouth Webster, all you've ever read is propaganda.

He calls the 1916 Proclamation PROPAGANDA! He calls the poems of Patrick Pearce PROPAGANDA! He calls the writings of Connolly PROPAGANDA . . . Go away, you're dealing with Webster now, not that rubbish over there, and Webster spoke on a Republican platform in Middle Abbey street which you've never done . . .

You don't even know what the cause is for.

I know what caused all your trouble.

Laziness.

Laziness. Well, I'm not competing with any Irishman. If you were born to work, you go out and do it. My share as well. St. Patrick wasn't an Irishman, but Ned Kelly who came from Fulham, he was . . .

You're a bastard, Webster . . . go on and admit it and save us the trouble of telling you.

None of us know who our fathers was, and we take a big guess at our mothers, said Webster. All right, let's take ANOTHER look at Ireland. In Northern Ireland, if you're a Catholic and you want a house, you won't get one. And if you're in Southern Ireland and you're Protestant, you won't get nothing. But England's FREE . . . If you want to worship in a synagogue, nobody will stop you. If you want to worship in a mosque nobody will stop you, but if you go to Belfast, they'll put you in jail for being a Catholic. If you go to Dublin, oh DIRTY DIRTY Dublin, they'll lock you up in a convent for being like Casanova, and they'll put you in jail without trial . . .

They put me inside in England without trial, Webster.

They did? that was for your own safety. Look, let me make one thing clear. Webster LIKES the Irish, that's why he knocks them the hardest. I am GLAD that the Irish are here, because Ireland is a land which produces saints and scholars, and LOOK, occasionally one of the scholars comes into the park. The rest of the time *Wimpey* employs all the saints. I love the Irish because my mother was Irish, only she was more intelligent than your mother. My mother came over from Ireland and had me here. Your mother had you in Ireland and then sent you over. That way she had to pay double fare . . .

Lomas came over from Lyons and joined them:

If the Jews didn't exist, Webster would have had to have invented them, Lomas said.

And then they would have had to have invented Webster, said Freddie Kilennen. Give him a break will you? He's not on about the Jews, he was on about the Irish as you said, and then this idiot started shooting his mouth off about England and now he's on about them. You listen for a change.

You want to see England's army, Webster was saying when they got back into the crowd, you want to see England's army? Go down Whitehall any day. You'll see it sitting on a horse in charge of a ruin. You ENGLISH . . . most of you are mentally feminine, that's why the Labour Party can come along and say VOTE THIS, and the Tory Party says VOTE THAT. Your minds are so damn empty that until the Labour Party puts a thought in it or the Tories put a thought in it, which is nurtured in your skulls, your skulls are the blank wombs of all this narrow nonsense that you produce. Why don't you start thinking a bit wider and get away from your narrow nonsense? What's the point of this world getting up and pointing to someone and saying he's a queen? a man like Oscar Wilde did more for this country than you'll ever do. Have you ever read *The Soul of Man Under Socialism*? Read that and forget your Labourism and your Toryism. Some of the greatest leaders in the world have been homosexual, and better than all your rubbish. WHO ARE YOU? WHO ARE YOU? WHAT ARE YOU? all you know is some poor little queen who comes into this park at night and starts playing with someone else in the crowd and OOOOOOOH, you're SHOCKED! Open those little heads of yours and see how filthy they are. The things which you attack most people for are things which you're most guilty of. So you attack the Jews, uh? So you attack the negroes, uh? YOU'RE AFRAID, and you put your fear outside of yourself; and because you're afraid of your own lack of masculinity you attack the homosexual. But the homosexuals are more men than you'll ever be. You've got collars and ties on and your name should be Mary.

When's he going to talk about the Natural Law Religion, said Cafferty, turning to Lomas.

He has to get through all this first, said Lomas. He's got to attack everything that he's believed in at one time or another, to stop them taunting him with having believed in it.

Webster had changed the subject to the Salvation Army:

When I was fourteen I was trained by the Salvation Army to be a missionary. I was going from England where everybody has got a shirt, to Africa, because I was told that little African boys don't wear shirts. Now that I've got older, I think that's rather a good idea because if little boys don't wear any shirts, and little girls don't wear any shirts they can see what they're having. With those things in front of me in this park, you get them home and you find that you're not having what you thought you were having. They get the labels wrong. The Salvation Army's way of thinking is that there is no REAL crime, no REAL wrong, as long as you've got something ON. They wear clothes through inhibition. I wear them because I don't want to shock you with my physical beauty. . . .

And when they came back from the catering stall, a man had been accusing Webster of being a traitor to his class. If he was born in Greyhound Road, Fulham, that meant, he was working class:

What is this rubbish of working class? Webster was saying, Every worker I ever saw tried to do as little work as possible.

Hardly one of you could work if there wasn't a boss to employ
you. If you were out of work tomorrow, you wouldn't have
enough initiative to sell matches. I was born over there, and this
is a royal park you know . . . belongs to the Queen and the whole
of the Royal family, and you know I never say anything against
royalty, why should I? they're OURS. We keep them.

I was born RIGHT over there . . . in a SLUM. It was a snob
wedding there if the bride was less than three months pregnant.
My mother was a good woman, yes, she was a good woman. My
father? he had not much brains. He had them in the same place
as a monkey with the result that he created a big family. I was
about the thirteenth, cheaper by the dozen. I was a WORKING
CLASS BOY . . . SO WHAT? the only people to get married
today are the working class. And the only reason the working
classes get married is in order to have a SERVANT. When the
upper classes get married they marry some tart, have her
company one week, divorce her the next. It's all the same.
FORGET this rubbish of working class. Did you ever see Ramsay
MacDonald living in a council house? forget your rubbish.
When I choose my company I choose the rich. The poor
embarrass me.

A man at the back interrupted:

When do we come to the subject? what about the Natural Law
Religion, or whatever it is, or is that just Webster?

No, my friend, the Natural Law Religion is not just Webster,
reaching down for his coat, putting it on and buttoning up the
collar. Webster is just one of the Natural Lawyers. . . . Webster's
a natural. But this is the Natural Law Religion: In order to live
you must die. In order to live, you must die . . . here's a bit of
christian teaching which you've never understood. See that tree?
it will get bigger and bigger . . . more and more leaves, and one
day it will be so big that it can no longer support itself. It must
die. Do you know how it will prolong itself? There's only one
way you can live into the future. You won't go to heaven or hell.

The only way to live into the future is with children of the body or with children of the mind. And as I can see you're going to have no children of the mind, you'd better get on with having a few from the body. This is the only immortality. This is the natural law. If you think you're going to survive the grave, go and sit in the graveyard for half an hour. This rubbish has been going on for long enough. The only punishment you'll ever know is here and now, and the greatest punishment is LONELINESS, loneliness in old age. The old people of England are the people who are suffering today. Why? because marriage has ended, family life is finished. They've spent half their time in bed for five minutes of pleasure. They then have to spend fourteen years slaving to keep some layabout in the sun, and when they've kept him for twenty years, he gets somebody else's girl, gets married and turfs the old man and the old woman out to bring the lodgers in. There is no family life left in England. If somebody's head gets in the way of the television set, they bash it in. Goodnight.

He got down, folded up his platform, took it to the alleyway behind the *New Inn*, and went back to his sister's place in Turnham Green where he was living.

What did you think of the Natural Law Religion? said Cafferty, when Webster had finished.

It's just Webster making a principle of Webster, Lomas said. You wait till next week, he'll have changed his views by then; there'll be something else chalked up on the board for him to get round to at the end of the meeting, when he's run through all the excuses for having been communist, muslim, fascist and God knows what else before.

The next week Webster still had The Natural Law Religion chalked up on the board, and it wasn't until the week after that it had changed to PUBLIC IMMORALITY, speaker WEBSTER. But as usual it wasn't until the end of the meeting that he got round to it. He had to contend with an Irish Catholic, who believed that Webster had deserted the Catholic church.

The man is tall and lisping and tries to inflict his sincerity upon Webster, seeming to think that his sincerity is irresistibly infectious and that there is a secret transfer of his beliefs which rise like mercury up the platform while he is in the meeting:

Look, Webster was saying to him, there is NO evidence to prove that there was ever an historical Christ. You're grown up now, do you want me to tell you about the three bears? if you don't want me to tell you about the three bears, why should you want me to jump into this nonsense about the Trinity? There is one God, Muhammed said it, and you can live for the next fifty million years and you can't make two. You can't make three, you can't make two in one or one in three or Watney, Combe and Reid. Just imagine God being one and getting hold of the other end of himself to look at the middle. . . .

We all accept its mystery, said the Irish Catholic.

WE ALL ACCEPT ITS MYSTERY . . . what do you think the Trinity is? James Bond? You and your priests, you come out here and say THIS IS GOD and offer me a drop of red biddy on a dog's biscuit. Your religion grew out of superstition and priestcraft because the church is a business. With three hundred million pounds of capital, they don't believe in the Holy Ghost, they believe in the trinity of rent, interest and profit. And where did the Church of England get their property? they stole it from the Catholic Church. One day these thieves will be turned out and it will be returned to where it belongs: the great mass of the common people. At the time of the Reformation in England . . .

I have a point, excuse me, said the Irish Catholic.

Well, sit on it. YOU'VE GOT NO POINT. The only point you have is so inflated with your own verbosity, that it would burst if you sat on it. At the time of the Reformation in England, that is the time of Henry the Eighth, they said in England that the Catholic mass was a blasphemous parody, and YET in spite of this, there's been a period of REVISION. Day after day you can't get on television if you're an atheist, you might get on once a year.

But every Sunday now we see the Catholic Church on television. Our monarch is sworn to defend Protestantism . . . THE CATHOLICS ARE CREEPING BACK. The Italians are coming here and every time they sell you ice-cream they give you a holy medal. The holy medal is to guard you in case you die from their ice-cream. THEY'RE ALL HERE WITH THEIR RUBBISH . . . and we English only became free when we threw the priests out.

They gave us education, said the Irish Catholic.

Who gave who education? What education have you ever had? I have none . . . I was educated in the university of life.

And you was sent down. What is this RUBBISH? Look at the parson who was tried the other day for corrupting boys, which is a kind of workday hazard for parsons. And what else did he do? he also helped the boys to pick out all the dirty bits in the Bible. What a load of crooks and scoundrels they were AND ARE . . . any dogged old parson going to challenge me? Any bald headed mullah? Joanna Southcott posed as a nude Virgin Mary. If the world is going to be full of nude Virgin Marys no one will know who their father was. Who's ever gone to heaven and come back to tell you? I know someone who went over to Ireland and come back. I know someone who went to America and come back . . .

How do you know he went? said the Irish Catholic.

I know he went, because if he hadn't have gone to America, the British wouldn't have known where it was to have gone after him. FORGET THIS RUBBISH OF ISMS . . . Catholicism . . . Protestantism. . . . In Italy St. Francis fed the pigeons because none of the other bloody Italians would. In Trafalgar Square you've got all the bloody Protestants feeding ALL the bloody pigeons . . . so it's all rubbish. It's YOU that matters . . . YOU . . .

No ism should be exclusively inward, said the Irish Catholic.

Webster paused for a moment, then turned to the crowd with a suffering expression:

I've known this man for years and he's a complete idiot. But he's a CATHOLIC, and he believes that Peter has the key, and only those who bribe Peter will be able to get in. And there's only one way to bribe Peter and that's by tipping the priest. Think of Webster knocking on the golden gate. If I get there I'll knock it off.

You'll need a skeleton key to get in, said the Irish Catholic.

NO . . . I WON'T need a skeleton key to get in because YOU'LL be in heaven and YOU'LL be a skeleton. There's no room in heaven for anything EXCEPT skeletons. You can't eat there. You can't sleep there. You can't have the other there. Pack it in. . . . When I used to pray I used to say Our Father WHO art in heaven. The Catholics say Our Father WHICH art in heaven. They pray to God as if heaven was on the underground. PACK IT IN. . . . Give them their sexual satisfaction and you wouldn't have this rubbish of saints. LOOK AT HIM . . . He believes in a universal religion, no ISM he says, should be exclusively inward. All right, I'm a Muslim Catholic and when I turn to pray to Rome, I find my grandfather was born in Jerusalem so I've made a racket and got the whole lot together . . . You'll learn one day that ideas and values are not to be picked up in any corner, they're to be picked up all over the world. I follow Mother Kali. I recite my rosary of skulls and one day I'll have your skull.

And then someone who knew that Webster hadn't fought in the last war came into the meeting and accused him of dodging the column:

I didn't fight twenty years ago. When I came out of prison in 1940 for I.R.A. activities in this park, I was considered non-combatant material, and they gave me a job watching idiots like you working. I was a Labour Supervisor in the West Country. No, Webster did not fight twenty years ago. The only fighting I ever did was in Fulham market when I was a kid, dodging under barrows to get specs. But there WAS a war, and there were generals in it who'd been in the last war and didn't die. The

Unknown Warrior, he came from Fulham, and nobody knows WHO he is now. My father, he was in the first world war: he knew nothing when he went and he knew still less when he came back. My brothers were in the first world war. Webster wasn't, and I learnt enough not to be in the second one either. The last war had nothing to do with Webster. It was between Churchill in his black velvet boiler suit, and Hitler.

Then some Arabs joined the crowd and accused Webster of betraying Muhammedanism.

The Koran says you should chop off the hand of the thief, Webster said to them. Do you think that's right today? Good God, if you chopped off the hand of the thief, there'd be nobody working in the Arab world. So, the Koran says you're going to flog all the prostitutes, so FLOG ALL THE PROSTITUTES . . . you won't have enough men to do the flogging.

So many moods that failed, said Lomas who was listening. So many moods that failed.

In this crowd, Webster went on, in this crowd there are Hindus who worship cows in India and go out with them in England. . . . We've got all kinds of creatures called Buddhists. They're the strangest of the lot. They never do anything. They sit down all night and all day to contemplate in their navels. Now Webster has looked in his navel for hours on end and never found anything really fascinating in his navel. I discovered that looking in other people's navels is much better. So I'm not a Buddhist, and I'm not a Muhammedan . . . they're queer. They have built in self-starters, they carry around their own churches. Oh the Catholic church is a dirty big church which they lock up at night in case anybody steals from the poor box. The Protestants have got churches too, but their churches are all offices for the Ecclesiastical Commissioners. But the Muhammedan, if he's got his carpet in his pocket he can bow down anywhere providing he's got a compass . . .

Who's paying you now Webster? said Freddie Kilennen, who's

paying you now that the Muslims packed you in? who's paying
you to speak on Public Immorality? the Messina Brothers?

Webster stopped and leant over the front of his platform:

They always come here with the minds of prostitutes. They
always wants to know who's paying Webster. Well, who's
paying you? where is that queer looking creature . . . who pays
you to come up here and interrupt my meetings? because who-
ever pays you, you're robbing them. You're taking money under
false pretences. When you can oppose Webster, you take your
money off them. Don't you worry who's paying me. All you do
is get what information you can on the cheap.

All right then, it's getting late and Webster's given you a good
run for your money, as no other speaker in this park would.
We'll talk about the subject now: Public Immorality. So,
LISTEN . . . I'm sick and tired of ladies who have no virtue in
them except their damn snobbery. I LIKE prostitutes, and what
belongs to them, let them sell it. I'm sick and tired of politicians
who are always selling what doesn't belong to them. These idiots
in Parliament shouldn't be allowed to stand up and talk about
something they know nothing about. That's not democracy,
that's mobocracy. Fancy following Macmillan, and what's that
other rubbish?

Dr. Crippen.

No, his brother, Mr. Wilson. What is this rubbish . . . and who's
that other one? HUME . . . spelt Home. That's the QUEER
thing about England. If a thing has got about fifty thousand
letters to it, it's called Chumley. It's tragic. It's time all the
politicians were let loose in the deserted areas of Scotland to
shoot ducks, shoot their mouths off and then shoot each other.

This is the meaning of Webster's Public Immorality: the
Christians are always denying sex and always indulging in it.
They spend three quarters of their life denying it and the other
quarter having it. The Catholic church looks upon men and
women who practise celibacy with the greatest respect. They

look upon nuns with respect whereas I look upon nuns as people who are WASTED. None tonight, none tomorrow night and none the next night . . . you might just as well not be born if you don't have none. And then again, look at the saints. All the saints are men who never had none either. St. Francis never had none. Suppose a priest today were to get up on this platform and preach the real doctrine of the church, the doctrine of Paul, that it is better to burn than to marry, and that if you go to bed with your wife you should get up in the morning feeling VIRGIN? If we'd followed that there would have been no humanity for all that to have happened to, two thousand years ago. What happiness would you get if you had to go to work every day? at a machine? or driving an engine? what happiness would you get if you came home every night to sausage and mash? The thing that gives you the greatest happiness is taking the girl friend to the dance. The thing that gives you the greatest happiness is that little walk home when you can give her the kiss of life. THIS is the beauty of life . . . there's nothing dirty or vulgar in it. This is Webster's Public Immorality . . . Goodnight.

Do you notice all the strange inversions of speech that people use when they've been speaking for a long time? said Lomas.

Yes . . . yes, said Cafferty. Lomas left with the rest of the crowd, and went off to his seat in the *New Inn*.

Webster began folding up his platform, surrounded by the few people who were left. One of them asked him why he spoke in the park, and Webster began explaining over his shoulder as he bent down over his platform strapping it up:

Don't ask me, why do you listen? I don't know . . . but I suppose when you speak there's a feeling under the ribs, under the ribs, under the ribs. You see, when you walk along the street placing the left foot forward, this is a masculine act. When you walk along the street placing the right foot forward, this is a feminine act; and when you stop to think about it, your feet change sex. Speaking is like this: sado-masochistic, and if you stop and think where the line of demarcation is between them, you get knocked off the platform . . . Hello.

Webster looked up at Cafferty.

Hello, said Cafferty.

What are you doing hanging around with that old crone Lomas? Does he feed you or something?

No, said Cafferty.

You know, said Webster, I've been coming up this park as long as he has and I've never heard him speak. He always lays down the law about how the speakers have gone off, and he's never spoken once from the platform . . .

He used to speak for the Syndicalists, said Cafferty.

Syndicalists? what Syndicalists? don't you come that rubbish with Webster. Do you want a meal? Carry my platform . . . he'll pay.

As Cafferty picked up the platform, Webster beckoned to an old man standing by the railings:

I want to forget the past, said Webster before he came. People are always coming up to me and saying: Webster, you made me a communist; Webster, you made me a fascist. So what? what can I do about it? he's a Muslim.

The old man was a Scotsman who was wearing a Muslim badge on his lapel. They left the park and went into a café off the Edgware Road; Webster ordered some sandwiches, peeled off the top layer of bread and smeared whatever was in them with tomato sauce. They talked for a time about the Muslim speakers in the park, and then the old man leant across the table and asked Webster what he was doing:

I'm curing a guardsman of a skin disease at the moment, said Webster.

Oh yes, said the Scotsman.

Yes, said Webster. Well, my father wasn't much use to me . . . he was an electrician. Mind you, being a skilled electrician before the first world war, that was something. But my mother . . . I thought you knew all this?

Webster turned to Cafferty:

My mother you see, before she was killed in the last war . . .
that's amusing, isn't it, it's usually soldiers who are killed in wars
. . . my mother, she was a professional healer. She was very good.
All the people round us in Fulham used to come to her when the
doctors couldn't do any more for them, and I do the same. I call
it hypnotherapy; I've been doing it off and on for years now. I'm
a hypno-therapist . . . it may sound phoney to you, but it's
nothing like psychotherapy or psychopathology or any of that,
you know. They have patients and so on, but their set brings them
within the orthodoxy. People just come to me when the doctors
can't do any more for them. I mean, this is the sort of thing that
you get happening. Some mother brought her boy in with
septic feet, and he'd got a load of bad blood due to an ingrowing
toenail. Now I used dream therapy, which enabled me to delve
right into his pre-natal existence. I discovered that he used to
masturbate, and I discovered that he felt very guilty about this.
He was also very conscious of having been circumcised. You see,
the blood and the knife, they are traumatic experiences. And
through the dream therapy I discovered that he had associated
one leg with his excretory organs and the other with his
sexual ones when he was in the womb; and, in his post-natal
existence, he had muddled them up. He projected his guilt about
masturbation into his feet . . . This was one of his dreams: there
were two dustbins and one was dirty and the other was clean.
Someone, he thought it might have been his brother, was hacking
at the bottom of the dirty one with a knife. This, you see, was his
toenail which he was using as a knife, and when I'd interpreted
all this I cleaned up his feet.

The Scotsman got up and paid for the meal with a note
from his spectacle case.

Do you want a cure? Webster said to Cafferty. You look pretty
diseased.

Where do you live? said Cafferty.

Well, I've moved to Bournemouth now. I come up to the park every week, but you come down to Bournemouth. The sea air will do you good.

Cafferty had a letter from him in the middle of winter from Bournemouth signed: *Webster, witchdoctor*, telling him his address, and saying that if ever he wanted to come down there he would make it possible, but to be precise about when, for he was often out, covening.

Webster was living in a boarding house in Donoughmore Road, Boscombe which is on the outskirts of Bournemouth, in a room at the top of the house with a piece of sticking plaster on the door and WEBSTER written on it in stale biro, Cafferty knocked:

If you're not a Tory, get out. I only mix with those that I can rob.

The room was as bare as the rest of the house. The landlady sat in the empty front room at the corner of a sandy carpet, with long white hair, a ruff of double chins, staring blankly at the blankness of it, drinking Camp coffee and waiting till the summer filled the house with buckets and spades and she could put the rent up. She was unaware that she had a tenant called Webster.

When Cafferty got inside, Webster was sitting up in bed sewing some new pockets on his trousers. He was hunched right over them, his spectacles had fallen down his nose bringing the operation out of focus and he sat there glowering in a thick pair of schoolboy pyjamas and a large green silk paisley dressing gown. He was expecting a patient. When the patient didn't appear, he suggested that Cafferty should make some tea while he got dressed and he threw him a tasbi as Cafferty left the room. It was a kind of rosary, made of large red beads, one bead separated from the rest with a knot at the end of it:

Play with that when you've finished, Webster said. The Muslims use them for praying with, but you can make your own god with it.

When Cafferty came back, Webster was dressed in his old tweed jacket and madras cotton shirt, but in another pair of trousers. He took *The Graphologist's Alphabet* from the table, rested a piece of paper on it and wrote a note to the patient:

I'm tired of waiting for you.

I'm teaching this patient to be aggressive, Webster said, and he stuck the note on the door.

They took the bus into Bournemouth and got off at the Winter Gardens.

I want you to be on your best behaviour, said Webster.

Where are we going? said Cafferty.

Nowhere.

They walked through the Winter Gardens until they came out on the Promenade and Webster began explaining why he had left London:

When that little Muslim Abbas issued a summons against me for assault, I told the crowd, and I could have had ten quid off them, couldn't I? If you want to make money on that platform you become partisan. That's the whole danger. That's why I've come down here. It was becoming a pro-Jewish platform. I'M not pro or anti . . . any pro or anti is rubbish. But I noticed that more and more Jews were coming to support me. Well that was dangerous . . .

I didn't notice them, Cafferty said.

You didn't look. It was like last year, when I was a Muslim, all the Muslims and that rubbish were coming round, and this fellow Abbas, he's a friend of yours isn't he? I've seen you talk to him . . . he wanted to get me hitched up to all those Cairo fascists, and when I wouldn't he goes round the crowd whispering Webster's a fascist. I mean, I learnt all this a long time ago. When the communists are against you, they don't say Webster doesn't agree with us, they abuse you, they say: did you know that Webster goes with little girls, or Webster's homosexual or Webster's in the pay of Cairo? I WAS at one time a paid speaker, but I chucked it. You don't want to depend on it, otherwise you start choosing money-spinning language.

He turned his collar up, wrapped his scarf round his chin, and stopped talking until they reached the end of the bay:

They either hate me or they like me in that park. I've made some bitter enemies. But then I'm a good speaker. I know I'm a good speaker . . . Bonar Thompson told me, he said: Webster, you're good and I had great admiration for Bonar Thompson. I mean, you saw him just walking round the park with his big brimmed hat and the long hair and you knew he was SOME-BODY . . . But he hadn't got this slick thing of the gutter which I've got. MacGuinness has got it.

Does the hypnotherapy connect with the speaking? Cafferty asked.

No, said Webster shortly. I mean I don't talk about it; they wouldn't know what the word meant. But then again it does, because I USE it. I spend twenty minutes talking rubbish and making them laugh and then, when I've got them laughing and relaxed, I slip in the poison that I want . . . like: There is only one God.

I mean, I treat them like that because they'll never be *important*. You don't think they'll be important do you? some of these Africans will though. An African comes to Hyde Park one week and the next week he's made Prime Minister. What could they be? you tell me, what could they ever be? they'll never even be the sheik of Notting Hill . . .

He broke off to point out two girls, they looked like au pair girls, who were sitting on the beach with their feet in the sand:

Look at them, you see, they're working class. I came down here to get away from the working class. They're like Narcissus the way they stare into the sea . . . I came from the working class, and anyone who comes from the working class either becomes a rebel, which is the same thing, because one can't exist without the other, or they work because that's all they're fit for. GIVE them work, but give them it NICELY . . . Those people there, they were working class. They had their feet in the sand. But they're happy until someone comes down here and spoils their fun with a red flag, and then they're marching and shouting all over the place.

They came to Boscombe Pier, and at the end of it was a roller skating rink. Although it was winter, the pier was still open and Cafferty suggested roller skating:

Pull your head in, Webster said. Don't come that rubbish with me; I'm not going roller skating with you until I can stand head and shoulders above you at that game. I'm not having you push me around as if I was your grandmother.

The patient had not arrived when they got back to Donough-more Road, so Webster suggested that they buy some food.

You carry the proletarian things, Webster said handing over the potatoes, and as they came back again he said that Bourne-mouth was, of course, a cemetery, but a cemetery where things could be made to grow:

You can smell money here, can't you? all these old bags of ninety with fallen wombs.

When they got inside there was a letter from the *Bournemouth Times* refusing to insert an advertisement for the Natural Law Religion, speaker: Webster.

I have to have my disguises, Webster said, tearing up the letter. Anything'll do: Natural Law Religion, Public Immorality. But always there's someone who's got some connection with the church who puts a spoke in it. If you want to book a hall you can't use the Natural Law Religion bit, you've got to put: Christos, the Natural Law Religion, and then put the sign of the cross on it, in the advertisement. It doesn't make any difference, it's only a meat skewer. Remind me to do it next time.

Webster's table was bare, save for his passport with his name altered from *John Alban Webster* to *John Muhamed Webster* and back to *John Alban Webster*; *profession*: *lecturer*. At the side of it

were two students' drawing pads, and on the empty bookcase
two crystal balls covered with a piece of flowery damask. The
crystal balls he said, meant nothing; but the drawing sheets he
used for what he called analysis by free association writing. As
the patient had not come he said that it would be a good idea if
Cafferty doodled for his interpretation:

Just doodle, Webster said. Just doodle . . . casually, while I'm
talking. Don't pay any attention to what you're doing. Just relax
while you're listening and doodle.

Webster went on talking about his plans for advertising his
practice in Bournemouth, and Cafferty said afterwards that he
had drawn some large cavernous shapes which grew complex
and then were cancelled out by their own complexity and
exploded by some thin strokes stemming from a plump maternal
shape at the top. Webster stopped talking to look at the drawing.
He didn't say anything, but changed the subject:

Do you dream much?

No, Cafferty said . . . at least I never remember them.

That's better. Now what was the last thing you dreamt? think
very hard.

I . . . I think I dreamt . . . no . . . I was a child, that was it. I
dreamt I was a child. It must have been during the war and my
mother took a room in Bolton, that's in Lancashire. There was
no electricity, just a spirit lamp, so that when I wanted to go
downstairs in the night, I had to go down in the dark because I
wasn't allowed to light the lamp and I didn't want to wake
my . . .

Is this the dream? Webster said.

No . . . this is reality. I'm coming to the dream. I dreamt that
when I came back from downstairs, the room was full of
Germans and my mother was gone. I put on a gas mask and then
I murdered them all with a flick knife. I think there was an old tin
bath they used to bath me in: I escaped by getting into it and
sliding down the stairs. I remember that it was an uneconomic

way to travel. But I know this dream occurred several years ago . . . I think I tried giving up flick knives in my dreams after they were banned . . .

It doesn't matter, Webster said, picking up the drawing. It doesn't matter how many years ago you dreamt it. It ties up with the drawing, all those cancellations. You're preoccupied with murder. You must know that. You're obsessed with murder . . . Look (he tore off the sheet of paper to reach a clean one), look, this is you in your pre-natal state.

He drew an embryo, Cafferty said afterwards, which seemed to be an extreme case of placental malnutrition, and which he provided with only one foot. He went through a usual, well-informed interpretation of pre-natal pressures, and then said that undernourishment at a certain point had accounted for the murderous instincts.

Did you ask him about the missing foot? said Lomas.

I did not, said Cafferty. I thought it no more than an oversight of his draughtsmanship.

That's very interesting, Lomas said. Because last week in the park, I distinctly remember him saying something to this effect: *The Lord's Day Observance Society* makes Sunday miserable for the great mass of the people who only had Sunday off, and it spends the other six days thoroughly enjoying itself. There's always a tiny minority who want to stop people. Somebody has only got one leg, so he starts an organization to stop cross country running . . .

It was getting late. Cafferty got up to go, but Webster stopped him and said: Do you ever get headaches?

Yes, said Cafferty. I've got one now.

Webster pointed to some mistletoe which he'd hung at the back of the door, explained its history: how the norse god Balda, who had been thought immortal, had been killed by mistletoe, and he told Cafferty that if he dreamt about mistletoe the headache would go.

And if you concentrate on the circulation of blood in your feet on the way back, you'll make doubly sure that it goes.

Cafferty dropped in the next morning, wanting to know his reaction when he was told that the headache hadn't gone:

No, Webster said. That was my little game, you see. I got you thinking about your headache and not your murderous instincts. THEY've gone. See you on Sunday.

When Cafferty came into the park the following week Lomas told him that Webster had rubbed off PUBLIC IMMORALITY from the board at the top of his platform and written WITCHCRAFT, speaker: WEBSTER.

Witchcraft? said Cafferty. He did have a copy of Aleister Crowley's funeral service programme, I noticed it in Bournemouth on the bed.

The man the *News of the World* called The Wickedest Man in the World? said Lomas.

Well, Webster didn't seem to think so, he kept quoting from this programme: Do what thou will shall be the whole of the law, and Love in the law, Love under will, or something. It was only a couple of pages long, written in torpid hymnal language and dovetailed into a couple of seedy pre-Raphaelite drawings. And then he kept muttering things about the seeding process of the nuclear society, or something, when he was talking about his hypnotherapy.

Yes, said Lomas. He was on about all that in the park today, and about teaching them to use will power passively. I couldn't make out what it had to do with witchcraft, but he was saying there was some connection.

When they went over to the park Webster was just finishing his meeting. He had dealt with all the people who felt that he had deserted their causes, or who wanted to know who was paying him, and he was able to get round to the subject written on the board.

I must tell these people about witchcraft, so shut your lug up
and get out, Webster was saying. I'm starting a coven. I'm
inviting them all, and you know when you go to a night club
you leave your hat in the cloakroom; well, when you come to
Webster's coven you leave it all in the cloakroom, unless of
course you're like Ghandi. Ghandi used to have extra wrinkles
to keep all his small belongings in.

Now England is getting bigger and bigger, like Queen
Victoria, but when England gets big something must happen.
Something must die so that a small thing can take its place. This
is witchcraft. That small thing is a seed, and unless the British
can produce a SEED, they will die with Babylon and with Rome.
We need a revolution of IDEAS not property. The seed is
growing, the seed is being nurtured in manure. BUT THE
SEED DOES NOT EXIST . . . you're overpopulating the world
with your nights out. Goodnight.

Webster did not come into the park for several weeks.

I expect he's building up his hypnotherapy practice in
Bournemouth, Cafferty said.

Hypnotherapy? Lomas said. Did he hypnotize you?

No, said Cafferty. I don't think I was a fit subject, but the
therapy part was all right.

Therapy? Webster?

Well, he got me to reveal my preoccupations, a few of them,
that's all any of them can do . . .

Why did you let him?

Well, he couldn't sell them.

A rumour circulated in the park that Webster was leaving.
Freddie Kilennen said that Webster had sneaked into the park and
given a short farewell meeting saying that if his crowd wanted
to ask him anything about his private life they were to ask it then,
and if they wanted to join in his private life, they were to ask
him after the meeting and he'd tell them how much it cost.

Also Webster had told Solly Sachs that he had got some money from somewhere, and that he was going to leave the park for good, give away his platform, and go away and die in a mosque in Istafan. He said he'd sit cross legged and die at the moment his beard grew to the ground. Solly said that he'd asked Webster what his farewell message was and Webster had said: To all Englishmen exclusively, Drop Dead.

Although Lomas hated Webster for his anti-semitism before the war, he thought that it was a pity that he was leaving the park. He decided to go and see him, and he found out that he was living in the part of Fulham which looks like Bournemouth, with trees on the sidewalk. Cafferty found out the exact address: Ranelagh Avenue.

Webster was living in a bleak first floor room, with large Victorian windows and bare boards. A pile of newspaper cuttings lay on the floor, and Webster came to the door with a bunch of them in his hand and a cup of cold lemon tea in the other:

So, Webster said, so, you heard I was leaving did you Lomas? you sloppy old thing. . . .

Are you leaving? said Lomas.

You mind your own business.

What are those newspaper cuttings doing? said Lomas.

These? I was just sorting them out, but now that you're here, I can convince you for good and all of the TRUE nature of Webster's past . . .

Truth is just something forced on people who aren't better provided for, said Lomas.

You wait. Now you're always saying Webster's a fascist . . . you wait, you wait. Sit down over there. Now where is it? yes, now this is a letter written by Mosley's right hand man to some idiot who wanted to know who Webster was, they were going to get me to speak for them. He gave me the letter. Here it is:

'*Sanctuary Press Ltd. Publishers of* Union, *incorporating* Action, *Price*

*twopence. 302 Vauxhall Bridge Road, London, S.W.1. . . . you asked
me about J. A. Webster who you said was a member of our movement.
Actually he never was a member as he had broken off all contacts with
movements of our kind, just before the formation of Union Movement
in 1948. For a year or two prior to that he led a movement of his own
in Bristol which expressed national socialist sentiments and was
extremely anti-Jewish. He was a very good mob orator and had
considerable following on the Downs at Bristol, where he held regular
Sunday meetings. We had been in touch with him as he said he would
bring in his movement together with a collection of many such movements up and down the country on the formation of Union Movement
itself. But only a few weeks before this was to happen, around Christmas
1947, he ratted from everything for which he had previously stood and
renounced all his attacks on the Jews from his platform in Bristol. We
can only conclude that the Jews fearing the formation of our movement
for the first time since the war, had suborned this man by a gift of money,
as they did not wish such a very good speaker to be at our disposal.
Naturally this action discredited Webster in the eyes of his supporters
who have now passed down one of his lieutenants into our hands.
Before long he left this country for Australia and this is the first we've
heard of him since he left. You will use your own judgment as to
whether you can trust him. Certainly you will have to take into account
the possibility that he might let you down at some critical moment. As
was the case in this country he is entirely dependent on the collections
that he can make at his meetings, on the other hand, he is a very good
speaker and might be made use of in supporting your aims and objects
always providing you bear his antecedents in mind. Yours in Union,
A. Raven Thomson. Political Director to Sir Oswald Mosley.'*

So you see, said Webster when he had finished reading. I was
never a Fascist. I admit I was anti-Jewish, I admit that . . . but I
was never a Fascist. That letter was to some idiot in Australia who
wrote to them about me when I was speaking on the Yarra
Bank. . . .

What about the anti-semitism? Lomas said.

It was a process of growing up, Webster said. Maturity means having the widest choice ... but I wasn't only anti-semitic, I was against *all sorts* of things. In Bristol I had this group FREE THE PEOPLE'S SUNDAY, and it came to a fight in the end between me and the *Lord's Day Observance Society*. I've got the cutting here somewhere, I was just reading it when you came in. Here it is: '... Stormy Scene. Police Intervene at Downs Meeting. ... There were women in the crowd which swayed to and fro as a mêlée developed near the platform upon which Mr. John Webster was speaking. A police officer forced his way to the centre of the crowd and whistled for reinforcements which arrived in a matter of seconds. The series of fights which had broken out near the platform ceased when the police arrived in strength and no arrests were made. The meeting was resumed after a break of five minutes, a large crowd gathered as soon as the meeting commenced and heckling was continuous. Mr. Webster's orange shirt disappeared as the platform was pulled down. The men hustled their womenfolk out of the crowd to prevent trouble. Mr. Webster, his shirt torn and blood on his face, smiled when he regained the rostrum. They can't stop me, I will be here next Sunday, he told the crowd. ...'

You see, Webster went on. I've always been against this kind of thing, these puritans. I don't change much. These puritans ... they've got warts on their noses and think they can't make love because of it. Bristol was packed with quakerism then, you know. The quakers were there before they discovered sex. The quakers are very much better now, though. They can join in with the best of us.

But I went on with my campaign FREE THE PEOPLE'S SUNDAY in the newspapers. One of the Lord's Day Observers wrote in asking them to stop my meetings, so I wrote an open letter to the Bristol paper. I've got it here: *Dear Mr. Wilmot, if you come to my house on Sunday, you will not find me on my knees all day. The Lord says you must not kiss on Sunday. Has Mr. Wilmot never been tempted to kiss*

a young lady on Sunday? or does he say: No dear, wait till Monday.
Mr. Wilmot wrote back: *I can kiss as hard as you and my wife's the same. . . .*

Why did you leave Bournemouth? Cafferty asked.

There was no one I could rob.

Who can you rob in Fulham?

No one you know. It's just old ground . . . old ground Cafferty.
Anyway they locked me up for using insulting words; I got one
month. When I came out of prison my face was scarred with
barber's rash due to the poisonous and unclean penny blades
which had been in use for about three months. I went back to
London to recuperate.

I've been more involved in this game than you have, said
Webster turning to Lomas. I've been doing these things for many
years. I don't change a great deal as a matter of fact. It's always
been fundamental to me: a respect for personal freedom. I
believe in the happiness of the individual, and religion in my
opinion means to live, and you can pray just as well having sex
as you can on your knees, because you can have sex on your
knees. I believe that people have the right to think and have new
ideas, and to meet new situations with new ideas . . . these things
have always been fundamental to me. That's why I've been
always in conflict, especially with priests, whether they call themselves mullahs, as with the Muslims, or they call themselves
fathers, with the Christians, without any babies, or whether they
call themselves policemen. I don't LIKE priestcraft of any kind.
Priestcraft to me means death by dogma . . .

Suppose you were going away . . . Lomas said.

Suppose I was?

Well, there would be no place for speaking.

Good thing.

They can't understand English in Istafan.

Good thing. I shall have to learn to get my sex in other ways
than speaking.

Webster got up and took the kettle out to the landing to fill with water. When he came back he found Cafferty looking through some of the cuttings.

I've been on the curing game for a long, long time, Webster said. It's not a new thing with me at all. Did you see this one? 'HEALTH AND HAPPINESS WILL BE YOURS THROUGH HYPNOTISM AND MESMERISM. NATURE'S MAGIC POWERS DEMONSTRATED. A NATURAL PATH TOWARDS THE DEVELOPMENT OF THE PERSONALITY BRINGING CURES FOR ASTHMA, RHEUMATISM, CATARRH, CONSTIPATION, UN-WANTED HAIR, sexual perversion, MIGRAINE, SPEECH DEFECTS. HYPNOTIST: JOHN WEBSTER . . .'

Why is sexual perversion in small letters? Cafferty said.

To draw attention to it, make them come to the meeting; and, at the same time to make them think that sexual perversion is normal, an everyday happening. I've got letters from all sorts of people I've cured. Where are they now . . . here . . . here's one: 'Dear Mr. Webster, since our telephone conversation the other day, a strange position has arisen . . .' Oh, yes, I remember that one. I cured the daughter and the mother became sick. But here's another one, and this'll show you that someone appreciates what Webster has done: 'To whom it may concern, Mr. Webster has treated me successfully for chronic asthma. The relief I experience after so many years is wonderful. I cannot speak too highly of these matters, or express how deeply I am indebted to him . . .' And this one is from the University of Queensland, which means that the man is no idiot in the accepted sense, even if he's an academic idiot. 'University of Queensland, Department of Physical Education.' He says: 'This is a brief note to tell you that the technique of auto-hypnosis which you taught me is extremely useful. I have been very glad to give up my time to attend your demonstrations. Up to meeting you my ideas on hypnosis were confined to the ideas expressed in the usual academic textbooks. Your demonstrations gave me my first insight into its practical application and value. . . .' That's a few testimonies to Webster's curative powers. The others I killed.

What is auto-hypnosis? said Lomas. How do you get out of it?

Well, said Webster handing out the tea, all the basic work was done by that old Russian Pavlov who said that it was all a matter of conditioning. You stub out a few reflex actions, that's all. The rest of it was done by Freud. His subconscious influenced the conscious mind of the day, and all that. Self hypnosis is just bringing about a condition of relaxation whereby you can get straight to the subconscious because the difference between the conscious and the subconscious is that the subconscious only reasons DEductively, from a point to a point, therefore any command which is given, which goes straight to the subconscious is automatically obeyed. Whereas the conscious mind reasons INductively AND deductively. It can arrive at a point of view which is essentially individual and for itself. It may contain contradictions, but from the subconscious there is only the automatic response to the suggestion which is fed into it by the computer. So if you have a crowd on the platform and you have them under hypnosis, and I always do, and you say to one of them: You are a dog, that person will bark even though he knows that he's not a dog. He's got to behave like a dog because he has accepted that suggestion.

All salesmanship, all oratory, whether it be a parson in his bloody pulpit boring his audience to bloody death, and making them want to die, by making them want to get away from his misery; or whether it's a heckler screeching with all the crowd giggling in front of him, this is hypnosis. And I'm always conscious of hypnosis when I'm on a platform . . . of deliberately utilizing an audience in this way. For example, I'll pick out one person. He will act as a scapegoat for the whole of the crowd, because then it will relieve the crowd to know that their own anxieties are taken away, piled on him, and they can all insult him through me. And if this is done with sense of humour in order to keep a balance in the crowd, it's PLEASING to the crowd, and quite often it's pleasing to the person I pick out because quite often they are masochists. When they are laughing at you along with me, they will know it's a beautiful day. . . .

Is this hypnotism? Lomas said.

Hypnotism is an unfortunate word, said Webster. It comes from the Greek . . . Some old idiot took it from the Greek. Previously it was called mesmerism after a man called Anthony Mesmer who used to go round magnetizing people with metal plates . . . animal magnetism. He had the idea off Paracelsus, who thought that he could transplant diseases out of the human body into the earth with a magnet . . .

That piece of tarmac in Hyde Park is littered with transplanted diseases from Webster's crowd, said Lomas.

Yes, Webster said. But Mesmer, he just left them floating round in mid air. I do the same. I like to call it hypnotherapy, it's all the same in the end. Relaxation . . .

But relaxation suggests that there is a residue of the conscious mind left, said Lomas.

There must always be a residue of the conscious mind left, don't interrupt, said Webster. This is why you say that even if a man is told under hypnosis that he is a dog, he knows that he isn't a dog, but the fact is that whenever the imagination comes into conflict with will power, it always wins. So, a person says: I will give up smoking, and he believes it firmly with the whole of his will, but he smokes the more because of it, because will power should be used PASSIVELY. It is the imagination which should be used in a dynamic and aggressive sense. If you want to accomplish something, you should think of how you're doing it, how you're living it, like an actor on the stage. This is what an actor is: a man who can live into his part, and if you want to accomplish something, you must live into the part of what you want to accomplish. This is what hypnosis does, so, when someone wants to give up smoking, he doesn't say: I'm going to give up smoking, he says: I'm going to give up smoking if I want to, it's dirty, it's not good for my health, it's very expensive, I'll give up smoking if I want to. I don't have to, of course, but I do want to for these reasons, therefore I'll smoke if I want to right now, but I won't smoke for a while; I can smoke later if I want to, but I don't suppose I'll want to even then. This way you can give up smoking . . . relaxation. I got Cafferty relaxed. He had murderous instincts. I cleaned them up.

So there is no difference between someone who is under a state of hypnosis and someone who is relaxed? said Lomas.

Oh no . . . no, no. You see, the whole principle of the world, in the main is a sexual principle: point and periphery, male and female, intension and remission, night and day. But in the human body, the whole of nature is essentially bisexual. There is no masculinity and no femininity, no complete night and day, no complete point and periphery, there is no complete . . . you see, they are constantly changing and interchanging, with the result that by relaxation we don't mean that the person has become completely relaxed so that he's no longer moveable or responding to anything; that would defeat its purpose. What we mean, what we mean is that he can become relaxed in a certain sense so that he can become acceptable to certain suggestions that are given to him, and then this suggestion must, of its nature, become dynamic, because this is where the imagination takes over as against the will power. The will power makes known its will, the imagination takes over and makes the wishes of the will power . . . makes them a fact.

I was never conscious of having an audience under a state of hypnotism, said Lomas.

I am always. You were a bad speaker if you ever spoke. You see, for me the platform is always a sex act. I DELIBERATELY provoke my audience so that they will come BACK at me, because I'm a bit of a masochist as well as a sadist. Everybody who starts speaking . . . you don't just start speaking because you want to. Practically everybody who starts speaking is a sexual PERVERT. And if you say this . . . if you say you're a sexual pervert to some of these people, this is a dirty word, and they think it means something you shouldn't do and if you do do it, you should only do it with your wife. That is the whole law of nature, the law of sex. This is why the fertility religion is the only . . .

But why platform speaking? Lomas said.

Platform speaking gave me in my early years the opportunity of expressing a personality. I didn't LIKE my father and yet obviously subconsciously I WANTED a father, therefore it led to my always rejecting God and seeking God. It led to an atheist, and nobody announces God more than the atheist does. This is the way my childhood started. I was very attached to my mother, I was very much opposed to my father. I never feared him, I was contemptuous of him, and this reflected itself later in my religion when I rejected the Christian god, because God was mixed up with my father. But all the time I was rejecting him, I was wanting a father, and this reflects itself in a thousand and one different ways. Right through my platform speaking even the things my opponents have criticized me for: Webster changes his mind, and so on: this same psychological fact has been with me the whole of my life, this continuous rejection and yet seeking after authority. I'm very conscious of these matters. On the platform I am the authority, and at the same time I'm usurping my own authority. This leads to doubts.

How can heckling and repartee be sexual perversion? Lomas said.

There's no such THING as sexual perversion, Lomas. This is a Christian INVENTION, there's no such thing as sexual perversion, provided you don't HURT anybody or do anything by FRAUD. These are the things I've had to work out. This is the key to my personality, and these other poor little creatures hate me because I know myself whereas they don't know themselves. They're Communists, Christians, Fascists or some other bloody rubbish because they are psychopathic, without knowing what can make them tick. I know. This is the difference. I KNOW why I am on the platform. I know why I'm enjoying it, and I know that I'm also a bit of a crusader as well . . . a person who likes the good things of life.

This word sexual perverts, Webster went on. I'm using it in a very BROAD sense. I used to know a communist in the park, he was quite an important man in his union, and he always appeared on his platform in a scotch kilt, though not many other people in the park knew what Webster knew about him. And then there was that man who was bent double, through foot fetishism. They used to call him the Hoop. And then there was that other communist speaker, a woman she was, and a cockney like Webster. She could never roll her R's. COMWADES, she used to say, COMWADES, come up to my WOOM. And when you went up there, she'd roll her R's all over the place . . . I've known most of the speakers and most of the speakers are sexually concerned with the park. They're either sexually frustrated, and screaming I LOVE JESUS, because they've got nobody else to love, or they're like the socialists. I mean I knew them all off the platform as well as on, and they were almost always what you'd call in modern language, kinky trade. There's nothing wrong with this. This is what made them into speakers, so it has a value; and when all these puritans talk about sexual perversions, what they'll do they'll turn the whole world into a desert. These are the things that the world *needs*.

So when a person comes for a cure, I don't try to cure him from something which in my mind is odd or different, I try to teach him something about himself or herself, so that knowing themselves they will consciously do the things they want to do, the things which will make them happy; and if I do this, then I think I succeeded in curing them. If they come to me complaining about their murderous instincts, then I tell them what the real meaning of having murderous instincts is. If they want to get rid of them, I help them to get rid of them. If they want to keep them, I help them to keep them. It's not my job to moralize.

My job is to teach, so that they'll realize their own personalities. If someone likes four women as against one woman, it's not my business to tell him he mustn't. My business is to tell him how to do it more effectively. Happiness doesn't mean that everybody's the same. It means . . . you see, these people teach what they call Christianity, and they never realize, these idiots in the park with the banners, that there's WISDOM in the bible, and you've got to let the tares grow with the wheat until the day of harvest, and you'll find that the weeds perform a very vital function . . .

Who are the weeds? said Cafferty.

The weeds? the weeds are nice smelling green things, just on the surface of the earth, which keep it moist, which allow the various mineral deposits to be taken back into the earth . . . the weeds give sustenance to what is considered . . .

Would you call yourself a weed?

Me? yes . . . I suppose . . . Yes, a weed, with deformed horns on. Yes, I don't mind what words you use. These are not important. All these words about weeds . . . some people cultivate weeds and others don't. It depends on who you are.

Lomas got up, yawned and stretched his legs.

It's getting late, he said. I think I better be getting along now.

Cafferty got up and put his coat on, and Webster came to the door with them.

Well, Lomas said as they were leaving, well, thank you Mr. Webster, thanks for the tea. See you in the park.

Yes, Webster said. But don't call me MISTER Webster. You've got nothing on me.

Van Dyn is a liar. MACGUINNESS

There are only two kinds of speakers in the park; exhibitionists who have something to exhibit, and exhibitionists who don't. Van Dyn has nothing to exhibit. WEBSTER

I bought a bar of Sunlight soap, some custard, sugar and a gross of small cardboard boxes. Then I made pills. VAN DYN

Van Dyn

JACOBUS VAN DYN is sixty eight. His head is shaved to keep a tattooed dragon visible at the back of it. His face is tattooed with bows and roses, hearts, flowers, twigs and butterflies, 'in pretty summer colours', as the tattooist put it. Large dots are tattooed on the edges of his ears and along his hairless eyebrows; a small moustache is tattooed on his upper lip, only, one better than Salvador Dali, it has four points: two pointing up, two pointing down.

The tattoos are fading now, as if they had been injected with milk, which Burchett, his tattooist, used to do when people wanted to get rid of their tattoos. His teeth are vermiculated, his nostrils loose and finger rutted, his eyelashes fixed to the lids by a thin yellow crust, his body white and flaccid. He bares the upper half of it for the tourists because a tattooed crucifix is spread across his back, surrounded by an aureole. The spikes of the aureole have lost their line with the shrinking of his flesh. On his chest he has the face of a boy tattooed with his lips surrounding a nipple. He is tattoed elsewhere.

To people, said Lomas walking away from one of Van Dyn's

meetings, to people strict in the choice of the company they keep in dark lanes on dark nights, Van Dyn's appearance runs against him. But in this park it's a commercial asset. Watch the people who come up to him and stare. Because of their sense of politeness when they find that Van Dyn is not an effigy, they have to talk to him. They have to pay for it.

Van Dyn, Lomas went on, quickly explains his financial position, and how they, as members of society are responsible for his condition as a criminal. Their figmented sense of guilt is rapidly dissolved by their purchasing power. It's a facile therapy, but as Van Dyn looks like a sea side postcard burglar (if you look at him long enough to forget about the tattoos), he fits well into the scheme of the transaction.

Van Dyn is the last of the personal grudge speakers. Do you remember the one before? Frederick. He dressed up in a green frock coat every Sunday, and brought a large blackboard into the park in order to demonstrate how Isaac Pitman had stolen his invention. He was known as the Trotskyist of the shorthand world . . .

DARTMOOR PRISON

I hereby certify I have this day discharged from custody F. 177 Jacobus Peters Van Dyn in consequence of Remission of Remainder of sentence. Given under my Hand and Seal this 3rd day of December 1931.

S. H. Roberts. Governor

CONDUCT WHILE UNDER SENTENCE: *Good.*

Van Dyn was sentenced to seven years' imprisonment in June 1931 for armed robbery. The police alleged that he held up a youth of twenty one, a waiter who was at the time using the name: Robert Paravicini Devin, whom Van Dyn already knew, that he knocked him unconscious 'with a terrific blow on the head' in a lane in Ruislip, Middlesex, and that he robbed him.

The Recorder, Sir Ernest Wild, ignored Van Dyn's alibi that he was first with two girls: Ethel Strachan and Phyllis Windle at Tower Bridge, and then that he had been in a lodging house, St. Christopher's Hostel, Upper Smithfield, when the incident was meant to have taken place, and said to the prisoner:

You have aggravated your offence by bringing forward an absolutely false alibi. Lucky for you that you are not charged with murder. In that case you would undoubtedly have hanged. You will go to prison for seven years.

The *News of the World* reporter described what followed:

Seven years! The sentence fell with stunning emphasis upon the hushed court. They looked at the prisoner. A flush had mounted to his heavy features, but not a muscle twitched. Actually he was smiling—smiling at seven years!

A warder touched his arm. He half turned, then swung to face the Recorder again. The smile was still there. 'O.K. Chief.' he said. Less than five minutes earlier the smiling prisoner had heard himself called: 'thief . . . procurer . . . blackmailer . . . ruffian.'

Van Dyn decided to appeal, but then he changed his mind after receiving a letter from one of the girls, withdrew the notice of appeal and submitted his grounds for appeal in the form of a statement to the Secretary of State. He wrote to the girl from prison:

I will not appeal if it is going to be inconvenient to you or cause you any trouble or make you lose your job. But remember 7 years is a long time and I know I'm going to die in prison as I have that presentiment and foreboding.

The Home Office investigated his alibis and he was released after having served only six months of the seven years' sentence. Questions were asked in the House of Commons, and the Home Secretary, Sir Herbert Samuel, made this statement:

. . . Van Dyn sent in a long petition to the Secretary of State asserting his innocence and reiterating the alibi he put forward in the Court.

Searching investigation was made by the police and my advisers, and, as a result additional information was brought to light. After consultation with the learned Recorder before whom he was convicted, I felt justified in all the circumstances in recommending the absolute remission of his sentence of seven years' penal servitude.

The implication of this was that Van Dyn was innocent, so he made an application to the Court of Criminal Appeal to have his conviction quashed. His counsel, Mr. Hector Hughes, submitted that Van Dyn's release indicated that, in the opinion of the Home Secretary at least, he was not guilty. He should therefore be given an opportunity to establish his innocence before the Court. He had been held to be innocent in one direction, although he had been held guilty in another, and that was incongruous:

Mr. Justice Avory: Why do you say that he has been held to be innocent? What has happened is merely that he has been released after six months' imprisonment.

Mr. Hughes: Only six months out of a term of seven years' penal servitude.

Mr. Justice Avory: Only six months! People do not serve six months' imprisonment for nothing.

Mr. Hughes: Presumably the petition which he had made to the Secretary of State has been under consideration and presumably the Secretary of State acted on the same advice in remitting the sentence . . .

And then Mr. Hughes went on to say that it would be contrary to natural justice to preclude Van Dyn from an opportunity to clear himself by having his appeal heard, that he was a Dutch Boer who did not understand our legal system, that he was convicted on the uncorroborated evidence of the prosecutor, which the Home Office had since considered unreliable (because they released Van Dyn), and that the Recorder of London was influenced by charges made by the police against Van Dyn, in respect of which he hadn't been tried or convicted, and which he denied.

Mr. Justice Avory, in delivering the judgment of the court, dismissed the case on the grounds that Rule 23 of the Criminal Appeal Rules, made under the Criminal Appeal Act 1907, provided that where notice of the abandonment of an appeal had been given, the appeal should be deemed to have been dismissed. He also pointed out that he thought that Van Dyn's excuse for having abandoned his notice of appeal, namely that the witness he wanted to call would lose her position, and her mother would go mad, was frivolous.

The reason, the judge went on, that the sentence had been remitted and Van Dyn had been released was that the Recorder appeared to have been influenced in passing sentence, by statements made by the police regarding Van Dyn's character and mode of life, and his previous convictions, which had led the Recorder to come to the conclusion that he was a thief, a black-mailer and a ruffian. But because of Rule 23 of the Criminal Appeal Rules, it was not necessary for the Court to consider the merits of Van Dyn's case. As Van Dyn had withdrawn his notice of appeal, this was the same as if his appeal had been heard by the Court of Criminal Appeal and dismissed. His conviction was therefore left on the record, and he was not entitled to compensation.

He has been claiming compensation in Hyde Park for over thirty years.

I was notorious as the ex-Capone gangster, Van Dyn says, and the police were determined to put something over on me. It was a frame up. I got seven years.

The case is only his excuse for being in the park, said Lomas, it's not his motive. He's not interested in establishing his innocence any longer; he just asks for the compensation. He's the only speaker in this park who speaks just for money and nothing,

nothing else. He comes before the police come on duty, and then he leaves when they arrive at about twelve o'clock in the morning. He's a good caterer.

Van Dyn said to the *News of the World* on his release from Dartmoor after his sentence had been remitted:

Bad I may have been, but procurer and blackmailer never. I cheated the procurers and dragged youngsters away from lives of damnation. If I had wanted to blackmail I could have got it by lifting a finger. But these hands are clean of all that, never mind what else they have done.

And he makes exactly the same speech in the park year in year out:

There's no point in changing my speech, Van Dyn said to Cafferty after a meeting. The ones who's heard me before ain't gonna pay me money because it's different, so I might as well repeat the same speech for the ones who haven't heard me before, and who ARE gonna pay me money. That crack about Oxford College is worth money to the Van Dyn stomach fund. Why should I take it out?

This is Van Dyn's speech. He stands on a tea chest which he brings into the park every Sunday, and he has a green carpet bag hung round his neck with letters and newspaper cuttings in to show the crowd:

Well now, ladies and gentlemen, when a man's in the park the first thing he's gotta do is get an audience . . . and to get an audience in Hyde Park, you gotta use psychology. And when you use psychology, you gotta apologize to the people in front of you because you don't want to give them a scare. Now what I'm gonna do . . . it's gonna make my voice a little bit bad, but I'm forced to do it . . . is to give a yell, and I'm gonna try and do it. Now I want you to see for yourselves what psychology does. Just come up a bit ladies and gentlemen. Don't be afraid of me. I ain't Oscar Wilde. . . . LADIES AND GENTLEMEN . . .

AAAAAAAAAAAAAAAAAAAAAAAH! Now that's all you
gotta do . . . here they are . . . you'll be all right.

Now ladies and gentlemen, Teddy Boys and Teddy Girls and
beatniks and other unclassified people. I welcome you to my
meeting. Now I do not talk about politics. I do not talk about
religion. Nor do I talk about anything that brings discredit to me
or anyone else in the park. Unfortunately the people here are
lunatics. The others don't know they are, but I know it.

Now I'm gonna ask you to do me a little favour. Right here on
this spot the Roman Catholic people comes and holds their
meetings. So I'm just gonna stand over there. I want to get away
from those people, because I'm afraid of them. If they bite me
. . . they get in an argument and jump down and bite me, I get
hydrophobia and I don't want to take that chance.

He gets off the tea chest, and kicks it along the ground, looking
over his shoulder to see if they follow:

Now ladies and gentlemen, in case you don't know who I am.
I am the man who was over there a second ago. Now my name
is Jacobus Van Dyn. I am known as the man who talks about
crime, criminals and gangsters. I am sixty eight years of age, or
will be on the twenty eighth of August coming this year. In that
sixty eight years I have spent thirty years in prisons all over the
world: SAN QUENTIN, BONAMORA, SING SING, I was there when
the Rosenbergs was executed, DARTMOOR, CENTRAL PRISON
PRETORIA . . . it would take a month for you to hear them all. I
don't boast about that. I was in the death house for three years . . .
THREE YEARS IN THE DEATH HOUSE OF SING SING
waiting to die like a mad dog.

Now I have no education. What education I have had I picked up
in reformatory schools and prisons all over the world. And talking
about being in prison, I don't boast about that. I incidentally was
in Oxford College and that's the god's truth . . . I was there only
a minute and a half when the burglar alarm went off and I had to
get the hell out of it.

I am the notorious ex-Al Capone gangster, but I could have been like you. One of my brothers is a judge in America. My two other brothers, they are lawyers, and here I am an outcast, a social leper. I ain't a bad fellow, honestly I ain't. Lots of people say: Oh he's no good. They ought to lock him up. But I come over here a honest God abiding citizen.

That lady over there says I ain't no good (*rhetorical*), I never been no good and I never will be no good; now, that lady is wrong. You've got no right to say that about me. Do you know why? there are only two kinds of people in the world today: those who's been in prison and those who ought to be in prison.

He gets off the platform and moves round the front of the crowd as he speaks, stopping to stare into the face of each listener. The front of the crowd is most likely to produce a few come-ons at the end of a meeting:

How did I start? Every dinner time when I came home from school, I used to go round the block on a postman's bike. They nicked me. My mother said: That isn't so, they've been doing it for years. Did they have the postman's permission? NO. And my mother spoke for me before the magistrate. They charged me with theft and they said they were going to teach me a lesson. They taught me a lesson all right. In that reform school I learnt how to crack a safe, make master keys . . . everything. They made me what I am . . . A NOTORIOUS OUTCAST. . . . A NOTORIOUS OUTCAST.

He gets back onto the platform, pulls a cutting from his carpet bag, keeps tabs on sympathetic eyes:

Now sir, you say: why don't I go back to America (*rhetorical*)? Look at this: here it is in black and white: 'He took nine lives through working for Al Capone. . . .' Do you think I'm proud of it? Of course I ain't. I was sentenced to death, one year awaiting trial in Raymond Street, Brooklyn . . . Judge Samuel Libovitch. Then I got a death sentence I was three years in the death house. I was there when the Rosenbergs was executed . . . also Fernandez.

I won my appeal, and I had another sentence passed at the same time as the death sentence: not less than seven, not more than twenty, for having a gun in my possession at the time of my arrest. They grabbed me for as much as they could: four years. I saw the parole board. They won't let me go back to America no more.

Here is a letter from the New York State Parole Board, Albany, New York, Head Office from my probation officer, a thoroughbred gentleman. Now listen: regarding your request to return to the United States, this is to inform you that if you re-enter this country prior to the natural expiration date of your parole, you will be shot on sight. How can they shoot me? I'm a public enemy in America. I am public enemy number six. I wrote to Mr. Hoover. I says, Mr. Hoover: why am I number six? a man of my notoriety ought to be number one. Don't worry, he says, when we bump the other five off you can be number one. . . .

He hands down the letter from the Parole Board. It is a brief acknowledgment of letter he has sent them, and mutters: You take that . . . don't you let them look at it. Don't you look at it either.

Next, he goes on, next I have a letter from President Wilson in the United States. He is a very nice man. Two years ago I wrote him a letter: Daddy, I'm broke. I'm a bum in Hyde Park begging pennies. I'm broke because I'm honest. I done you a good turn, you ought to do me a good turn. I ought to tell you what the good turn was. Wilson became President when Taft died. On the day of the election I voted for him fifteen times on the ballot papers that I got, and under fifteen names. He sent me fifty dollars . . .

Now that man over there says I'm a rotten old thief (*rhetorical*). He ought to be locked up, he says. Now that man's got no right. What is wrong with being a thief? I saved a lady's life the other day through being a thief. She went to a psychiatrist in Hanover

Square and the psychiatrist said to her: You've got all the money in the world, you've got all the places in the world; unless you have something to worry about you're gonna die. So I done her place, took some jewels and gave her something to worry about. Not one of you in this audience has the right to say I'm bad. I've paid my debt to society. Have you done it?

I am here to try and get society to pay its debt to me. I was wrongfully convicted in nineteen thirty one and sentenced to seven years. I was released after six months, and no explanation. I was notorious as the ex-Capone gangster, and the police was determined to put something over on me. It was a frame up. I got seven years. I am trying to get a few bob together to go on with my fight.

When we come here . . . the speakers, we take a chance in going round with a little bag. It is the privilege of a speaker. Over here it's against the law, but we take a chance. I'm trying to get a few bob together so I can have some picture postcards printed of myself which I'm allowed to sell right outside those gates. There goes the first gentleman . . . he's going away. That's all right, he's taking the train to Aberdeen. Then after the collection I'm gonna strip . . . show you the crucifixion on my back. Now please, I don't insult you. If you don't want to put anything in the bag, it's a free meeting. If you haven't got anything in your wallet, put your hand in somebody else's; and if you don't know how to do that, stay behind at the end of the meeting and I'll teach you.

He gets off the tea chest, and shifts quickly through the meeting with a green *Barclays Bank* cash bag. He zig zags round the semicircle. The crowd unplaits and wanders away. Van Dyn looks around for the come-ons. There are none. He spills the contents of the bag on top of the tea chest:

Get me two teas. One without milk . . . five lumps of sugar. Don't go off with the money because I split bloody nothing there, and I've got something to tell you when you come back.

Cafferty came back. He had forgotten. He drank the tea, stared
in front of him:

The Singing Woman . . . get that collection away before that
singing bitch comes.

He is terrified of two things in this park, said Lomas. He's
terrified of the Singing Woman, because when she starts to sing in
someone's crowd, and she wanders away, she can pick a crowd off
a speaker; and he's terrified of the police, but they've only given
him a summons for collecting three times in thirty years, and
with the one that came up, he was only fined a quid for it, and a
week to pay. Van Dyn's got no friends, friend. The police are
the only people he talks to; he can't have a relationship with
them based on money, and he talks to them more than any other
speaker in this park.

Thanks for getting the tea, said Van Dyn when Cafferty came
back with the tea. It's played out here . . . proper played out, and
my voice has gone. Even the underground's in a hole and all
that. You know, a man come up to me the other day, and I
recognized him from a long way back as Mack the Snout, and he
said: Give me five bob, so I said: I haven't got it. So he said: all
right, I'll stop you from having a meeting. I'll break it up. I went
up to the copper anyway, and he said: What did he look like? I
told him, and he said: You know, you get more trouble from
your own people than you do from us.

Then he takes the two cardboard tea cups and walks over to
the Coloured Workers Welfare Association, stands under the
platform, places the cups inverted on the ground, and brings his
heel down on them in turn, so that the air is compressed, the cup
tears and explodes. Mr. Mathews, the speaker, says: SHUTUP
. . . SHUTUP . . . you second hand monkey, you poor white
trash. This is OUR country, and I am the Lion of Judah.

Then he goes over to Axel's platform, and shouts: WHY
DON'T YOU GO BACK TO RUSSIA? and Axel looks at
him and says: You be quiet, or I'll show you where I'M tattooed.

I'm going back to the Rowton . . . you're allowed into your cubicle after one o'clock on a Sunday. . . . I'm gonna go back for a kip. See you next week.

He stuffs the bank bag into his pocket, gathers the newspaper cuttings off the tea chest, picks it up and walks out of the park.

He walks along the subway to the tube station. Two girls walk past. As they are coming by, he says: . . . So anyway, I sees these two girls coming towards me, and I takes a fireman's hatchet and chops their heads right off their bodies. You should have seen the mess.

He does not look at them as they pass. He does not look at you. He knows that you have heard him say that countless times before, and the girls' reaction was there before he said it.

Van Dyn was called the Dutch lieutenant of Al Capone and he WAS in the death house in Sing Sing. I read it in a newspaper. An American tourist was talking to Lomas in the *New Inn*.

Get away, said Freddie Kilennen, he was a kitchen clerk in Johnny Farmer's kip house in the *Seven Dials* all the time he was working for Al Capone. Get some more to drink.

Was it in one of the cuttings Van Dyn brings up to the park? said Lomas.

Yes, said the American.

Well, Lomas said, those cuttings are just cuttings about the park. When the newspapers have got nothing on, in the silly season when there's nothing on, they have a list of things to fall back on: the illnesses of Royalty, cancer cures, drug racketeering, the people who've given a date for the end of the world, and Hyde Park. Then they come down here and record everything everyone says. The only thing Van Dyn has ever stolen is his own mind.

The American bought some drink and left shortly afterwards.

Is there a secret Van Dyn? Cafferty said.

No, said Lomas. He's been saying that he worked for Capone, that he's spent thirty years in prisons all over the world, and that he's the world's worst man for so long, that he believes it all, and nothing will budge him. That case of his thirty years ago, that must have sparked it off. Then he found gradually that he could make more money out of a crowd plugging that line, than by saying that he was just another innocent man found guilty and not given any compensation.

The secret Van Dyn? Lomas went on. He just wanders round London tapping people until it's time to go back to the Rowton. Go down to the Rowton . . . three or four well annotated ideas on the nature of poverty and a few assumptions borrowed from the footnotes, and you've got what the sociologists would categorize as a field for research into the poor of London. Hire yourself a self soaping Orwell complex and go and prove the truth of their categories.

I've been there before, said Cafferty.

The Rowton House is a turreted building with five storeys overlooking St. Mary's churchyard at Newington Butts. From the Elephant at night it seems that a vast, clogged sheet of stamps has been hung between Dante Street and Churchyard Row. The light shines through the perforations. The lights are on in most of the slit windows.

The entrance is in Churchyard Row, and if you want a room you have to wait until all the occupants have rebooked their rooms, or handed in their keys and collected their key deposits. The hatch clerk then checks through, when the internal queues have finished, to see how many rooms are available.

A notice swings on the door: BEDS AVAILABLE on one side, HOUSE FULL on the other. A cartoon from a newspaper has been cut out and stuck onto the HOUSE FULL side. A man is bound up in bandages from head to foot with only his face showing, and his whole body is hung horizontally in the air with ropes and pulleys. A doctor is standing by him, and saying: Sorry! we've run out of beds! The notice is supported by a single twisted string, and sometimes swings back to front when the door is pushed violently, but it isn't a live issue.

The internal queues finish, and the men waiting for cubicles outside the turnstiles, file up in front of the office:

Name?

Davies . . . are there any specials left?

Insurance card?

I haven't got it with me . . .

Been here before?

Yes.

The clerk disappears, goes across to the filing cabinets, and brings back a card:

What was the address of your last job?

I worked for *MacAlpine* on a job in Kennington Road.

Right . . . There are a few semis at twenty seven and six, and some specials at thirty five bob.

Special.

The man hands over the money. The clerk gives him his ticket with the Rowton regulations printed on the back: The bedroom must be vacated before nine o'clock in the morning, and remain unused until four-thirty every day, except Saturday and Sunday, when it can be used after one p.m. Smoking in bedrooms is strictly prohibited. Ticket-holders are not allowed upon any bedroom floor other than the floor upon which their own bedroom is situated. Visitors are not allowed in the bedrooms etc. etc.

Next . . . name?

Bolling . . .

Bolling? Bolling . . . Unwanted Admission?

No sir . . .

Bolling . . . Bolling . . . Albert Boll . . . 'fouled sheets and cigarette damage. Nineteen, seven, sixty one.' Out.

No, no sir. It wasn't that. I gave the key, you see, to a mate of mine in Gordon Row to look after when I was . . .

OUT. Next. . . . name?

Cafferty.

The last time Cafferty was here he did not run into Van Dyn at all. This time it was three weeks before he ran into him in one of the corridors. There are a thousand and fifteen cubicles; mostly they are filled.

He was standing in front of a notice on the wall: ANYONE SPITTING WILL BE EXPELLED, and pointed it out to Cafferty as he passed. It is a reminder that you can walk out of the door whenever you want. He said: It should be Anyone FOUND spitting will be expelled. It's ungrammatical. But he went on staring at it. There was more authority about it with the word missing.

You know Tattoos then? Bishop was saying, the Governor's best boy? Van Dyn only lives here because it's like the nick, what he's never been in. He calls the Rowton porters screws behind their backs, and then I went down to the communals with him one morning for some of their slimey, and he kept on saying we was on esso . . . association.

This was Bishop who has lived in the Rowton House for nine years; an ex-prize fighter, with his name somehow still on the register, who worked as a cleaner in a gymnasium in the Old Kent Road. He had the next cubicle, and was talking out of the windows after they'd been thrown out of the communals at half past ten. He stuck a pin into the end of his cigarette and stared out at the churchyard trees. Clothes had been flung out of the windows and hung on the trees, slooped and frozen at the ends of the twigs. He rubbed the glowing tobacco core between his fingers and dropped it down:

And never give Van Dyn cigarettes. You know when he asks you for one, he says he's going to keep it for later? He does, doesn't he. He saves them up until he's got a packet and takes them down Gerry's café in Crampton Street and flogs them. I mean I've tried to interest him in some of my little schemes . . . a

shilling roll-up on Wayward Queen last week and he'd have
won five. I told him. That's a nice bit of cloth you're wearing,
ought to have it made into a suit. Tell you what, I'll give you a
dollar in the morning, see what you can do with it; and don't
get taken for a ride by Van Dyn . . . this is the first and last nick
he's ever been in. He's been here since nineteen twenty five, it's
all in the books in the office, and that's the only life sentence he's
ever had. Capone? that's the name of a pork pie hat. Why else
would he live here if it wasn't like a nick? you pay the same per
square foot in here as you would for somewhere up West, and
you can't even use it for a lumber . . .

1909: Reformatory school till aged 16 for theft.

*1909 (again): Three years in Breakwater Institution, Cape Town,
for common assault in the Reformatory, the term to date from day
of conviction.*

*1914: Aged 17: sentenced in Central Criminal Court, Johannes-
burg to three years' hard labour for breaking into His Majesty's
Empire Theatre and other places.*

1920: Fourteen days for disorderly conduct (gaming), Liverpool.

1921: Four months for theft in Liverpool.

*1923: Fifteen months' hard labour: Liverpool Assizes for theft by
conversion.*

*1927: Three months' hard labour, Marlborough Street Court,
London, as a suspected person.*

*1928: Nine months' hard labour London Sessions as a suspected
person.*

*1929: Eighteen months' hard labour and fifteen strokes with the
cat at the Old Bailey for robbery while being armed.*

It is on record that I laughed at them when they flogged me
that dinner time at Wandsworth Prison. Thereby hangs a story,
Van Dyn said the next time Cafferty saw him in the Rowton.

He wouldn't tell you any more about that period, said Lomas.

They coincide with the Capone era in the States, his convictions in South Africa, Liverpool and London. Van Dyn's only a circus criminal. When you go back to the Rowton take a pin with you.

A pin? said Cafferty.

Yes, Lomas said. Lombroso has examined the general sensitiveness of skin in sixty-six criminals, and has found it obtuse in thirty-eight of them, and unequal in the two halves of the body in forty-six. His conclusion was that as they had no feeling, they didn't understand pain in others. Van Dyn is quite human.

He doesn't talk much when he's outside the park, said Cafferty.

No, said Lomas. I don't think I can remember him ever saying anything outside the park. No, wait I can remember something: I think someone had him up for tapping in the street, and he said: When I'm broke he gives me money, and when he's broke I give him money. We have a pattern.

When Van Dyn was released from Dartmoor in 1931, he told the *News of the World* that he was going to call at the Home Office for a passport, collect some funds and get out of the country. The *News of the World* described him at the time as having 'a powerful build, lank black hair with a bald patch on the crown of his head, a wide mouth filled with perfect teeth, a flat well hammered nose, and frank, brown eyes.' He went to America.

Well, I said to myself, that was easy; and it was, Van Dyn was saying. You see, boys, only five days ago I was in Southampton England, and now I was sitting in a restaurant down by New York City waterfront. Sure it was easy. In Southampton five days before, I had walked aboard the old *Mauretania*. I had a sweat rag round my neck, my face blackened a bit . . . no one questioned me as I walked aboard. I went down below to the fireman's quarters. I found an empty bunk and went to sleep.

Next morning I went into the mess hall, sat down and had a good breakfast, then up on the after deck. The ship was due to leave in the morning. I was still on deck when she casted off. At twelve midday I went below and joined the black gang that had just come off duty, had a meal with them and went into their quarters, found an empty bunk and went to sleep.

This process I repeated till the *Mauretania* docked in New York City. Then I just walked ashore at dinner time. No one questioned me. I went into Olivers Restaurant across from the dock, bottom of West Fourteenth Street. I had four pounds ten . . . this I changed into U.S. money.

Well, what now? I said to myself. I little knew then that I was to run into adventures that was unbelievable. Already I was confused by the hustle going on around me. Everyone was in a hurry. This (I got to know afterwards) was one of the ways of getting the dollars . . .

Van Dyn was chopping a green NO WAITING sign with a hatchet as he spoke. He works from seven in the morning at Mahoney's timber yard off the Walworth Road bundling sticks to supplement his old age pension, and relays of kids stand in the doorway staring at him. One of them, Colin, had his name tattooed on the ball of Van Dyn's right hand. This was to commemorate an occasion when they had bundled fifteen crates of sticks together. Mr. Mahoney had said that that was a record.

Colin looked at the other kids and asked Van Dyn what his first job was in America:

Well Colin, Van Dyn said, you've heard this story before, but it was working for a tourist guide in Chinatown. I had to stand in a shop doorway all day in Matt Street and this is what he told me: First, he said, get a vacant look on your face. This I did. That's good, he said. Now, bring your fingers up to your nose. This I did. Now shake your head. Now repeat, now repeat and keep on repeating. That's good, he said.

Well, this guide . . . get on with bundling some sticks, will you? I ain't talking for nothing. This guide then returns with a party of tourists. Ladies and gents, he says, please take a good look at that man in the doorway. Don't go too near him. See him? see how he is hitting his nose with his hands . . . the uncontrolled shakes of his

head? Well, he is a dope friend, a hop head. He is one of the
Bowery's lost souls. Pray for him.

From grafting he moved on to dipping wallets at Sacco and
Vanzetti protest meetings.

When did you go back to straight thieving? Colin said.

Well, Van Dyn said. It was when I was in Los Angeles. In Los
Angeles I get into a house one night . . . it was not a very big
house, nor a small house. In the living room was piled many
articles of all kinds. I saw by the cards they were wedding presents.
Another table was littered with the remains of a feast. The
wedding cake remains was in the centre. I went upstairs and found
myself in a bedroom. Two sets of pyjama suits was on the bed. A
man and a lady came into the room . . . I can see their feet. They
kissed, and the lady said: thank goodness that is over. I am glad
too, the man says. Let us go to bed, my turtle dove . . . Then I
went on from there. I once broke into the house of William
Randolph Hearst, and brought out a fortune in antiques . . .
couldn't get a dollar for the lot.

To avoid arrest he became a hobo and hopped freights back
across America with a seaman who had killed his captain by
filling his whisky bottles with water, and he gathered up a few
qualifications necessary to present himself on the Chicago scene.
He was a sparring partner to Jack Dempsey at Proctors, and he got
to know all the fighters:

Boys, the world will never know again such fighters as there
then was. I remember them all: Harry Grubb, Young Stribling,
Mike McTique, Soldier Bartfield, Benny Leonard, Lew Tendler,
Louis Firpo, Kid Norfolk, Pancho Villa, Ted Kid Lewis, Harry
Kid Berg, and the never to be forgotten Battling Siki. I stayed
one time at the same hotel as Siki. He had won a fight and he had
changed fifty dollars into nickels. Now a nickel is heavy; Siki
threw hundreds of these nickels onto the heads of youngsters who
had gathered under his window. Many of those youngsters were
hurt. Their parents come after Siki, but the cops convinced them

that Siki doesn't mean no harm. Poor old Siki, he meets his end via a knife stab in the back in Hell's Kitchen. They gave him a grand funeral.

He presented himself in Chicago as South African ex-Middleweight champion, tough guy and con man:

I saw Texas Guinan, Van Dyn went on, Texas Guinan . . . get on with bundling that wood will you, Cafferty? Texas Guinan of Come Along You Suckers fame. She was a swell lady. I spin her a tale and got a hundred dollars from her. She told me: Look, I believe you. Here is one hundred. If you have caught me for this one hundred, then I am the sucker. May her soul rest in peace. . . . No, don't bundle them like that, you always break the rubber bands if you do it that way. It ain't no faster; I've told you about that before. Why can't you listen to what you're told?

Nobody knows whether he was ever in America, said Lomas when Cafferty came into the park. All the chronology's muddled up. He could have gone there when he was a seaman in between his convictions; he could have gone there after his case in 1931. When was Sacco and Vanzetti? And he could have worked for Capone though I've never heard him say what he did for him it doesn't matter. If it's a lie, there's a truth hidden in it: it reveals his preoccupations . . .

Shut your face, Freddie Kilennen said. It's his line . . . it's his graft.

But Van Dyn began to talk about Capone once in the radiator room in the Rowton late one night. The story would have gone on for longer, if the porters hadn't been sending the lodgers upstairs:

I don't care if you believe it or not, Van Dyn was saying. What's it to me? What do I get out of it either way? You're skint. Anyhow this is the story, Cafferty. Once Al Capone, three of his gorillas and myself are en route to Florida, you see. We passed a young fellow flagging cars, and Al says to the driver: Hold on, that kid looks . . . get away from that radiator, will you? you can dry a handkerchief out on it in fifteen seconds and it's burnt away in under a minute. . . . Hold on, Al says, that kid looks as if he can do with a drink. It was bitter cold. Al said: Get in. This youngster was a clean cut type . . . he did not know Al. Al asked him: What are you doing in this part? and the youngster replied: I went to Chicago to join up with Al Capone. Al Capone looks at the youngster, he looked hard. When we got to the next town, Al says to the youngster: I want you to make me a promise, will you please? Well promise me to forget about ever trying to get money by dishonest means. Al gave him five one hundred dollar bills and told him to take a bus home. . . .

Come on Tattoos.

Yes, all right . . . all right, we're going.

I've heard Van Dyn claim to have been a friend of Dion O'Banion's, said Lomas.

Well? said Freddie Kilennen.

Well, said Lomas, if he was a friend of Dion O'Banion's, his attitude to Capone must have been pretty ambivalent. I mean, Capone was never directly implicated in O'Banion's murder outside his flower shop, but it was pretty clear because he inherited the jurisdiction of the two warring gangs: O'Banion's and Torrio's, and Torrio was forced to flee by a man called Hymie Weiss, but before there had been a careful balance of power. Capone, he would have foreseen all the consequences of the murder, and the consequences were that he scooped out both the scales.

He could have been a friend of them both, dear, said Freddie Kilennen. Van Dyn can be friendly at times.

Well anyway, said Cafferty, the period leads to some good, old style policy statements:

Van Dyn is back in Mahoney's timber yard. He picks up a

bundle of sticks, fits them into the stick bundler with his carious
hands, levers them together in a tight, splintering knot, and then
nips a band round them and carefully counts it into the crate:

Boys, in Chicago during the Prohibition period we had many
a shooting scrap. You see, we put it this way: we had to kill or
be killed. And besides, if we didn't defend our boss's goods
against hijackers, the chances was that the syndicate took good
care of us by giving us a one way ride. It was all in the game;
besides, the District Attorney of Chicago, Mr. Swiggin, said as
long as these gangsters kill each other, we don't mind. They are
helping the law in their own way.

Now boys, as I've told you before, I was sentenced in New
York City to not less than seven and a half and not more than
twenty, and when I was arrested I was in a bad state. I was hopped
up with drugs. I was hopped up rotten, and I couldn't get out of
the habit, and I done some foolish and rotten things which I
know. . . . What are you doing? don't chop the wood like that,
you'll lose us the job. Chop it straight, will you? Chuck out the
bits with the knots . . . as I said, I done some foolish and rotten
things, which I know my maker will forgive me for. I wasn't
responsible, boys. I couldn't buy the cops off. . . .

Did you ever shoot anyone? said one of the kids.

Boys, I did. I won't tell you about the incident in detail, but
these two guys, they came for me. They went for their guns. I
never gave them a chance to pull them; I fired through my coat
pocket. I got them both. They never knew what struck them . . .
never ever came off that shooting for those were the days.

What happened when Capone died? Colin said.

Then there was no protection, said Van Dyn. Then I found
myself in Sing Sing, Auburn, the Tombs, and all over. The
protection ran out, and the money ran out. It was the same for all
of us. Take the case of Gerald Chapman. He was charged with
killing a cop and sentenced to hang. He appealed and appealed
and his last appeal was based on the grounds that the State of

Connecticut had no lawful right to carry out a death sentence on him until he had served his life sentence in Pennsylvania. Now, this raised a legal point. But they put a fast one over on Gerald. The President of the United States gave him a pardon from his sentence of life in Pennsylvania which gave Connecticut the clear of way to hang him, which they did. He was a clever crook all right, but he lost out in the end. There were others like him . . .

Who was in Sing Sing with you, Van Dyn? said Colin, looking at the other kids.

Lucky Luciano was in Sing Sing with me, and members of the Brooklyn branch of Murder Incorporated. That's who was in Sing Sing with me.

What's it like in there? said one of the kids.

You could wear your own clothes . . . that is to a extent. Get on with the bundling.

Van Dyn got up from the log he'd been sitting on to chop the wood, and bent down going through the pile of sticks for knotted ones. He gathered up a handful, sat down by the fire and fed them into it one by one.

I used to kill time by various ways, Van Dyn went on. For instance, I used to march from end to front of the cell a thousand times. This generally took all of the morning. I used to make up stories . . . put myself up as an imaginary Emperor, and think up things that I would do to make my country better. I used to count the bricks on the walls.

And then when they let you out, you come back to England, didn't you? said Colin.

That's right, said Van Dyn.

He had himself tattooed (the operation cost around a hundred pounds), and appeared in wrestling booths as the World's Worst Man, and then he got himself a huckster's stall in Petticoat Lane selling cough slum, pills and horse shoes:

Now why is a horse shoe lucky? Van Dyn used to say to the people round the stall. It is lucky because when Our Lord ascended into heaven a rainbow appeared in the skies. But this rainbow was upside down . . . a horseshoe. People looked at it as a good omen and from then onwards kept a horseshoe nailed upside down on their doors. Now ladies and gentlemen, maybe horses at that time did not wear horse shoes, but who knows? Take the case of the cross eyed lady last month. This lady was born cross eyed. She was so cross eyed that she always banged into people. The doctors could do nothing for her. She bought a horse shoe charm from us. One night she fell from a step ladder and the shock from the fall put her eyes right.

He never gives any reasons for why he was crooked, does he, Lomas said.

He doesn't speak much, said Cafferty, only for money in the park, or to keep the kids bundling sticks for him. A couple of sentences now and again, two or three changes of facial expression, and that's your lot. He's an old man.

Sociologists aren't having his subconscious on the H.P., Lomas said. They're just buying labels, and it's their own motives they ought to be studying. They're just labels, what Van Dyn says, you forget the word patterns. Have you ever heard him say: I feel this or I feel that?

I haven't, said Cafferty.

Ah, shut your face, Lomas, said Freddie Kilennen. You've heard him tell them in the park time and time again why he went crooked. I know it off by heart: I have been asked many a time: how come a man of your intelligence turned crooked? I guess it was written in the books, who am I to fight fate? When I went out thieving, I didn't go out to rob the poor. I merely relieved that class of the community that has too much wealth than is beneficial for its health . . . All that, you've heard him on that one, course you have. . . .

The murderer from Beuthen, Lomas said thoughtfully with his hands cupping the glass, the Beuthen butcher, he said that when you kill a man it is not much different from slaughtering a pig. There is a little white foam, and then all is over.

For Christ's sake, said Freddie Kilennen. For Christ's sake, shut your face.

The kids had gone home for supper. Van Dyn counted the crates again, cleaned up the table with the bundling wrench on, swept the chips off the floor and shovelled them onto the fire. He stood and waited until the flames had died down.

We didn't do too bad today, kid.

No, said Cafferty. No . . .

The Rowton rent is due Saturday, always remember that kid. Pay your rent and all else follows.

Yes, said Cafferty.

He picked up the poker and pushed some of the unburnt chips into the bottom of the grate amongst the crumbling coals. They flared up and died, like sulphur.

Why do you speak in the park? said Cafferty.

In the park I tell them about prison. I tell them that the prisons in my opinion should be torn down for all the good they do. I tell them that they serve no useful purpose. You are put in there because the law says you must go there. Everything from then on is just routine. The Minister comes because he has to, and that goes for everyone. They like that, they like to feel that they put me there, and by giving me money in the park they're getting me out again. That's what they think and I don't mind. It's worth a couple of bob.

He took his coat off the hook, padlocked the gates, and they went round to Mr. Mahoney's house to give him the key and collect the money.

You can never get to know Van Dyn, can you, said Bishop leaning out of the window at the Rowton. He's the same every day, he says exactly the same things, he does exactly the same things. All he thinks about is the law in the park, and the rent.

He likes food, said Cafferty.

You know, Bishop went on, when I first came to the Rowton he used to shove a notice under the door reminding me to pay the rent. I knew him from the park, you see. Nine years ago, that was. That is the most important thing, he says, when I see him again: Pay the rent and all else follows.

He's a nutter, kid, he's a nutter. He wanders up and down the corridors waiting for someone to start coughing, and that's not long in this dump, and then he shoves notes under the doors saying how he had a gypsy friend who gave him some very good advice. The gypsy told him that if ever he had a cold, to put some cold water in the palm of his hand and sniff it up his nose and that he'd be surprised at the result.

And I'll tell you another thing, he makes the other speakers very suspicious of him in the park, you know, when he goes on talking to the law, and then pretending to be so cagey of them when he goes round with the bag. That's what makes them think he's never screwed a place in his life. 'Killer speaks in Hyde Park' . . . all that. He's a good grafter, I'll say that for him, he's a good grafter. Don't get me wrong, I like him. . . . I like him. Hang on a minute, will you? don't go away, I've got something in here . . .

He disappeared from the window and Cafferty heard him unlock the cupboard in his cubicle. Then he reappeared with a cigarette in his mouth and a green jacketed book in his hand.

A mate of mine give me this book when I was up West. He's a dealer in them, you know. You read it and then you lend it to Van Dyn. Give it him if you like, I don't care what happens to it. It's about screwing places, and screwing a bit of the other thrown in. What did you do with the dollar I give you? Give him the book . . . soon tell whether he's a villain or not. Goodnight.

He handed *The Thief's Journal* across the window sills, closed the window, got back into his cubicle and started tearing up pieces of newspaper and wedging them in the gaps between the frames.

Goodnight, said Cafferty, and he crawled into bed. He read the book and thought of it in connection with Lomas, the pin, and Lombroso.

Herbie Bishop said you had a book to give me, said Van Dyn in the park after collecting one and seven pence. Well kid, I'm going back to the Rowton now for a kip, a bit of a kip. This park is played out. But it's all right, I knew it would be today, look at those clouds. So, I asked Mr. Mahoney to keep me Saturday's money till Monday, before I get my pension.

Parney? did you know that word? that's what the speakers say when it's raining. They say it's coming down to parney. And then you've got a whole lot of things like that. A Noah's Ark, that's a nuisance in the crowd. . . . Noah's Ark, Hyde Park, it goes on from there, the rhyme, until you get to heckler. And the edge, do you know what that is? that's the crowd. When you say I'm going to scarper the edge, that means that you're getting rid of the crowd. Now that, that was a dead edge I just had, that was a crowd that couldn't be bottled . . . so, I scarpered the edge.

I'm going back to the Rowton now, but you can give me that book if you like. When are you coming back to the Rowton? All right, well, I'll push my bed up against the door you see, and leave it just open, so that when you open it, I'll wake up. I'll leave it so the door moves just a space, and then none of those bloody drinkers can come in and persecute. You can slip the book through the gap . . . I like a read; you can have the light on all night there if you like. I like a read.

The door banged against the metal bedstead:
Yes, what is it? what's the matter? Oh . . . Cafferty. . . .
He yawned and got out of bed.

I thought it was that Maltese ponce across the road. He's always knocking on my door, and someone nicked that cutting of mine: '*Cannibal King From England*' . . . that one, the one I used to show the people in the park. I used to tell them I was gonna sue the magazine for libel, and all this and all that . . . have you got the book?

Cafferty handed him the book through the door. The room was almost completely dark. One of his Blackfriars Settlement suits was hung in front of the window, and all that was visible was his white night cap, and the gaps between the tattoos on his face, which showed up like chipped tracery.

Thanks for the book. I'll give it you back down at Mahoney's. . . .

He put his head round the gap in the doorway, and looked down the corridor, his eyes screwed up and blinking:

Boy, I'd give anything to be in Sing Sing at this minute. Do you know what they get for dinner there today in all probability? Chicken Fricassee, white Maryland style, Corn on the Cob, Virginia baked ham, Roast Pork chop, French fried. There is Sauerkraut pizza pie . . . and my favourite dish: Pastafazoola. The Irish ain't forgotten either . . . always for them: Corn beef, potatoes and cabbage.

Cafferty looked down the corridor.

It's all right boy, the screws don't come round for a bit, and the governor's in bed now. . . . And while you eat, the music plays. What do you want more? Now you've got a cell there that's just as good as a house, and five times the size of your cubicle. You've got a flushed toilet. Then you've got a basin with boiling hot water. The water is so hot that you can make any kind of beverage you want . . . cold water too. Then you've got a spring bed, spring mattress, pillow, and at the back you've got your radio earphones . . . The Mutual and National and American broadcasting companies. Heater . . . you can switch it on up to a hundred degrees. There was a one way glass into the street. I used to stand in front of it in a vest and G-string looking at the people in the street blowing the tips of their fingers with the cold. What more does a man want than that?

Anyway boy, don't let the screws catch you on the wrong corridor. Thank Bishop for me, will you? I like a read. I've learnt a lot from reading. He's stubborn, Bishop. He's been more times Unwanted Admission for not paying his rent than anyone. I tried to straighten that kid out, but he wouldn't have it. I done my best for that kid and now he's got the law after him, and this ain't a clever place to be with that hanging round you. Goodnight.

The next day at Mahoney's Van Dyn did not mention the book. He was concerned that he and Cafferty break the record of fifteen crates set up by him and the boy, Colin. The boy came in late in the afternoon, when ten and a half crates had been filled. Van Dyn brought out some bread and treacle from a carrier bag, and paid the boy what they owed him from the last week.

Do you want some? he said to the boy.

I bust up my transistor, said Colin. It fell on the floor. Will you tell mum that you busted it?

All right, we'll get you straightened out, Van Dyn said. Have some of this.

The boy cut himself a slice of brown bread and ate it. Then he left.

The pile of crates totalled fourteen and he came back.

I told mum that you busted it . . . she said you wasn't to come up the house for meals no more; and then I went into Mrs. Freedman's shop, and she said that you wasn't to come up there no more, she said you was a dirty old bum . . . and I think I'm packing it in and all, don't get enough money. You can stuff the wrestling tickets.

Van Dyn watched him go, gathered up the stub of bread, the treacle and the knife, chucked a couple of wrestling tickets on the fire, gave the grate a kick to even up the mound of smouldering wood, and left.

They went back to the Rowton and sat down to have a meal in the communal:

They water the tea, they water the rice, they water the porridge, they water every bloody thing. . . . The wrestling . . . Doctor Death was going to be unmasked this time, I could see that coming.

He pushed his tea and steak pie forward on the table and took out a biro from his pocket. With his head bent forward and his hands just below the level of the table, he rubbed it backwards and forwards on the word Colin, tattooed on the ball of his right hand.

I'll get it lifted out, he said. I've had lots of names tattooed, and then I've had them lifted out.

He moved to the television room. The volume and the channel are decided on by the old age pensioners in the middle of the afternoon. They stay there all day with the volume at maximum level, and the heat and foul stench builds up until they are thrown out to go to bed, their eyes streaming with the smoke.

Wrong channel, Van Dyn said. And there's no way of getting it changed. Try and ask them to vote on which way they want it. You'd get your throat cut.

A man was lying outside the reading room in a pool of vomit. One of his mates took a sheet of newspaper from the reading room, tore out a semi-circle and laid the rest of the paper round his head. Van Dyn walked past him saying that it was his policy never to get involved with people in the Rowton, always leaving early in the morning and coming in late at night. They went into the reading room.

Van Dyn found two empty chairs at the end of the room, sat down, put on his spectacles and pulled the green jacketed book from his coat pocket.

We could get a price for this book, kid. Bishop's gone . . . done

a bundle . . . a really nutty book, really nutty. Did he read it, kid?
I expect he read it. *The Thief's Journal* . . . listen to this: 'There is a
close relationship between flowers and convicts . . . Should I have
to portray a convict or a criminal, I shall so bedeck him with
flowers that, as he disappears beneath them, he will himself
become a flower, a gigantic and new one . . .' You don't want to
tell people that, you'll have them all at the racket. And then he
says criminals are remote from you . . . as in love, they turn away
and turn me away from the world and its laws. Theirs smells of
sweat, sperm and blood. In short, to my body and my thirsty soul
it offers devotion. . . . That's screwed up, ain't it, Cafferty. Did you
read it boy?

Yes, said Cafferty.

Well, it was very wrong of him to give it you. He should have
given it to me direct. He knows me well enough by now.

He flicked through the pages of the book.

I'll produce this book as evidence when my case comes up,
Van Dyn said.

When your case comes up? said Cafferty. It was in 1931, they'll
have forgotten about it by now.

I haven't forgotten, Van Dyn said. I write to the Home
Secretary every month . . . always get an acknowledgment.
Still keep on with it.

What good would that book do you? said Cafferty.

I don't know, kid, said Van Dyn, but it's proper screwed up
. . . proper screwed up. Did I ever tell you about Tin Tack Harry?

Yes, said Cafferty.

Van Dyn paused, pinched his nostrils and lobbed the mucous
onto the floor. Tin Tack Harry was in Dartmoor with me at the
time of my case. He always spread tin tacks around the beds of
the sleeping persons into whose houses he broke at night.
Naturally the cops knew who he was, you see, and went after
him. He didn't mind. He was happy.

This guy, he is like him . . . dressing all these crooks up in flowers and all this and all that. He seems to like being caught. When I was caught it was an accident. I once broke into the house of William Randolph Hearst, and brought out a fortune in antiques. I couldn't get a dollar for the lot.

He took off his spectacles and put them into their case.

Yes. . . . He'd give us a few bob for the book, a few bob. I come away from Mahoney's with five bob a day, they let you earn more, that's all they allow me to earn, you see; otherwise they'd lop it off my old age pension.

He looked around the room.

It ain't a bad old place, this, is it kid . . . ain't a bad old place. I could get a room somewhere else you know, oh yes, and for the price . . . get a room for twenty five, thirty five . . . But they say it's difficult to fit me into rooms with the tattoos . . . the landladies say that.

The lights were being turned out, and some of the men were gathering up the newspapers from the tables and the floors to take up to bed.

It ain't a bad old place . . . I remember a flop house in the Bowery where they used to stretch a rope across the room and you'd hang across it, with it under your arm pits, and your arms dangling on the floor. In the morning they just cut the rope. Screws . . . screws, come on, gotta get to bed. I'm gonna shave my head. Bishop said my hair was too long and you couldn't see the tattoos at the back, the dragon. Pay your rent and all else follows. Goodnight.

ALAS, POOR JACOBUS!

A former Chicago gangster is in Chingford trying to get a price on his head. He wants to sell it to 'Professor' Ben Gunn, a Chingford tattoo artist, on a pay-now-collect-later basis.
Reason 68-year-old South African born Jacobus Van Dyn

considers it so valuable is that it is the world's most tattooed head.
'Professor' Gunn told the Chingford Guardian *that he and a*
German tattoo artist would buy the head for about £25. After
Mr. Van Dyn's death it would be skinned and stuffed by a
taxidermist and would be exhibited.
'It is common practice in Japan,' said 'Professor' Gunn.

Van Dyn was away from Mahoney's and the Rowton for about
three days. When he got back he walked into Mahoney's, handed
Cafferty the newspaper cutting, took out the tin bath, filled it
with logs and started chopping them silently.

Gotta beat that record today, gotta beat that record. And I
ain't paid the rent yet, and then I fall out with the governor, and
all this and all that.

He went on chopping, slivers of wood hitting the cobbles with
a bony sound.

Didn't make out in the end, Van Dyn went on. He was a
pupil of George Burchett in the Waterloo Road, was Ben Gunn.
Burchett of course, he's been gone ten years now. He did the
tattoos in the first place, and Ben Gunn's been very good to me.
But I lost out in the end . . . said he hadn't got room for the head,
and all this and all that. He's only got a little booth. Cost me a
hundred pound to have it tattooed in the first place. Should come
back at me with interest. Give me the cutting back will you, I'll
show it to the people in the park.

Over Christmas the Rowton was decorated with a Christmas
tree dabbed with cotton wool and stuck behind the benches in
the white tiled hall, and red crêpe paper hung across the ceilings of
the communals. Van Dyn came in from Mahoney's and stared at it:

I don't send anything out, he said, and nothing comes in. That
way people can have the same opinion of me as they have the
rest of the year, and they do anyway.

The next day he walked up from the Elephant to the park and

made a speech worth two shillings and seven pence, a French franc, a luncheon voucher, and a note written on an empty cigarette pack saying *Go Home*.

He had stripped for the crowd. The temperature was below freezing. The speech was the same as usual save for a brief postscript. He had been having blackouts at Mahoney's and in the Rowton due to undernourishment. The crowd was small and shiftless; they were waiting for the other speakers to arrive. There is no one who comes to the park regularly to listen to Van Dyn.

Now ladies and gentlemen, thank you for the money, that will help me to get straightened out a bit. Now I have been speaking all over the world. I have spoken at the Irving Statue in the Charing Cross Road and at Tower Hill wall. And when I was at sea, I spoke on the Boston Common, Massachusetts . . . Union Square, New York City, Pershing Square, Los Angeles . . . in Sydney's Hyde Park, Australia . . . on Cape Town's Market Square . . . in front of Johannesburg's Town Hall steps and in front of the City Hall Durban . . . and . . . and of all strange places; on the Market Square Abadan, and that is on the Persian Gulf.

But I first started speaking in this park thirty two years ago when I was released from Dartmoor after wrongful arrest, and it was under that very tree that I'm pointing to over there. That tree . . . And I have been getting hold of the feeling lately that I'm gonna die under that tree. Thank you.

He gathered up his things, handed over the tea chest that Mahoney had given him to the man with feathers in his hair, and began walking back to the Elephant, staring into cafés on the way, and looking for one where he said that the proprietor wouldn't refuse to serve him. He passed about half a dozen places, until he came to one in Villiers Street, at Charing Cross. The proprietor there, Van Dyn said, didn't think that a tattooed head put people off their food, and had expressed this opinion many times.

I know what they say about me, Cafferty, Van Dyn said bringing the teas to the table. There are more things said about Van Dyn than there are Van Dyns to live up to them. It's the tattoos. I know what they say; they say: there's that old bum up there talking, and then they see me again, and they say: there's that old bum up there talking again. Yet on the other hand, this what you're talking to, this is the most famous face in London.

He bent down to his tea:

I KNOW what they say about me, Cafferty. They say that I was selling pamphlets at Tower Hill, on how I led the prison riots at Dartmoor, all the time that I was meant to be working for Capone. I did both, didn't I? And all the rumours about what Van Dyn does when he leaves the park, and all this and all that. . . . I KNOW it. I know it . . . how he ain't got no feeling, how he's never done nobody a good turn in his life, and all this and all that, and how he ain't got no friends. What do you want friends for when you've got a head like mine? . . . It's screwed on proper . . .

I didn't say anything, said Cafferty.

Well, you was about to, Van Dyn said. You have said before that you don't believe I ever worked for Capone. I heard you. I remember these things.

Yes, said Cafferty.

Well, I'll tell you a story, that will convince you that one of those things that they say about Van Dyn is wrong.

All right, said Cafferty.

Van Dyn pushed his tea aside and leant forward, talking softly:

It was in a small town in Georgia that I was passing through, when I was in America, and I saw a crowd of people . . . most were armed with guns. They were marching a terrified young negro through the streets. I followed. They took him to a small school house, and inside I heard a woman shout BRING HIM OUT . . . WE WANT TO SEE HIM DIE. Then everyone shouted the same command. They brought him out. Some men broke down a wooden privy . . . make a ladder from the wood, place it against the school and force the negro up. They have chains on his hands. They make him sit astride the top of the roof, and they nail the chains down. They pour kerosene and gas into the schoolroom and set it alight. I heard the young negro shouting Please have mercy, O God. Please have mercy. A man shouted back: Did you show mercy to the school matron that you outraged? NO . . . NO . . . NO. The flames now around that poor man . . . I thought that I saw one of his eyes pop out. I get sick in my stomach. I turned around again. Everyone is shooting at the negro. I noticed a young boy about eight or nine years of age . . . he was shooting too. He had a big shot gun that was bigger than him, and every time he fired, the recoil knocked him down, but he just got up and fired again. . . . At the end, kid, there wasn't nothing left.

No, Cafferty said.

I couldn't tell that to the people in the park.

Why not? said Cafferty.

Why not? Van Dyn said, because they would walk away. I've told you why I like to stick to the same things. That joke about Oxford College . . . I incidentally was in Oxford College. I was only there a minute and a half when the burglar alarm went off and I had to get the hell out of it . . . Why should I take that out? That is money to the Van Dyn stomach fund. They like that.

He paid for the teas, nodded blankly at the proprietor and shuffled his things off the table. They got onto Charing Cross bridge and he picked up the thread again:

They say these things about me. It's professional jealousy, you see. They don't have the claims that I have. Well, we'll go back to the Rowton . . . get a free Christmas dinner Wednesday . . . you don't. Free Christmas Dinners for the old age pensioners . . . you'll have to age a bit.

He turned away from looking into the river, clutched his carpet bag with the newspaper cuttings:

If I'd never worked for Al Capone, kid . . . but, I did you see, I did. I worked for Al Capone ten years: three years a truck driver, three years a body guard, three years a courier. And one day Al sent for me and he said to me: Van Dyn, take that money on the corner of the table, take that wristlet watch. I did, and blew it. Take that stack of money . . . no, I already mentioned the money . . . Take the ring, he said. Take the ring, I want you to get out of America, go anywhere you like. I says: What's wrong Al? He says: the F.B.I. is after me, income tax, and I cannot beat that rap. It's a federal rap. There now. Don't ask me about it again, kid.

They reached the end of the bridge, went down the steps and walked over to the Waterloo Road. They passed St. George's Circus and got into London Road, Van Dyn as usual was silent. He stopped once or twice on the way to bend down and cough violently. They reached the Elephant, and then Newington Butts and the Rowton. Van Dyn turned to Cafferty as they went in for Christmas:

Kid, Van Dyn said putting on his spectacles and looking up and down the letter rack, kid, if I'd never worked for Al Capone as I said; they'd nick me as soon as looking at me for obtaining money under false pretences in that park . . . No . . . no letters. See you, and you can tear the blood off me if that ain't true. They'd nick me for obtaining money under false pretences.

The Park

A COLD Sunday evening in January. Cafferty wanders out of the poulticing heat of Lyons across to the park. The trees are bare, the grass worn to caked mud. Few landmarks at this place, to settle quarrels over speaking pitches for example; only people, railings, trees, a couple of notices, and a refreshment stall.

He wanders through the meetings.

Somebody asks MacGuinness whether he has ever been on the needle. I was once, he says. It shut me up. It wasn't me.

Van Dyn says the park is played out and that he's going to see if he can't put the bite on someone outside Cash Cooper's tattoo shop in the Arcade in Coventry Street.

Axel says that there is no need for another Shakespeare. The other was complete. That is the beauty of a genius, that you don't need two of them. They are a present that the world only needs to be given once.

Cafferty joins the queue at the refreshment stall, and takes a cup of tea from the waitress. The woman at the till looks up at him as she presses the button.

Is your name Cafferty?

Yes. . . .

We've got a letter for you, haven't we Joyce?

The other waitress hands him down a letter. It is an airmail letter from Pakistan, addressed to him care of the Town and County Refreshment Stall, Marble Arch.

Greetings you, it runs, *from the shores of Pakistan (Arabian Sea). Thanks to Mr. Muhammed John Webster, who introduced you to me in absentia. I was very glad to learn that you were interested in Islam— the Religion of Peace. I am a Graduate with Honours in Mathematics and am interested in the Comparative Study of Religions, Science, Travel, Pen-friendship and the Religious Interpretation of Science. Says Quran, the Scripture of Islam: Wa ta'awanoo 'alal birre wal taqwa. (And co-operate for the goodness and piety) Chapter 5: verse 3. So let us co-operate for the furtherance of Truth by understanding Islam—the Religions of Peace, its principles and practices. Hoping to hear from you. Thanking you. Yours Brotherly in Humanity . . .*

Take your thumb off the signature, Freddie Kilennen says, looking over his shoulder.

Cafferty takes his thumb off it. It is written in Urdu.

So Webster's left the park then?

Looks like it, Cafferty says.

MacGuinness is back on the surgical spirit, the jack stuff. He has a friend at the moment who's persuading him to filter it through a loaf of bread, cut at each end, to catch the poison. But the friendship won't last, or else one of these days he'll run into a sliced loaf, and he'll kill himself. It doesn't matter much. It doesn't matter at all. Lomas was looking for you.

Oh. Where is he?

In the *New Inn*.

They leave the refreshment stall and wander across the tarmac. The man with the silent message is standing in silence on his milk crate by the gate. A man says: Don't you want any followers?

The man with the silent message draws back his cuff with his long forefinger and looks at his watch.

He has to drive them away with a stick, another man says.

What'll you have, Cafferty? Lomas says.

Webster's left the park, says Freddie Kilennen. Cafferty had a letter.

Is that so? says Lomas. May I see it?

Cafferty produces the letter.

You know, Freddie Kilennen goes on, he was here only three weeks ago. He was saying that if the Jews didn't exist we would have had to have invented them . . .

And you said that then they would have had to have invented Webster, Lomas says. Yes, I remember. But if you had read this letter carefully, you'd have seen that it doesn't say that Webster's in Pakistan. Didn't you notice his platform in the rack in the alleyway as you came in? Anyway, if he's gone, he'll be back.

Lomas gives a tired look round the bar: the trite, bored look of a man whose hair is falling out, or whose bank balance is wilting.

So, Lomas says, turning to Cafferty, so, you have discovered that MacGuinness is a drug addict, and that they put him in the madhouse, which they call a hospital because they're handing out monopolies of reality to psychiatrists; and you've discovered that Axel talks and talks and talks and talks, because he believes that secrecy is anaemic, and that he wants to be king of the world; and that Webster thinks he has the crowd under hypnotism and that if they don't believe that they can come and see him afterwards and he'll make them believe it with his crystal balls, which, I read lately, some very reputable psychiatrists use along with pentothal to cure amnesia or loss of memory; and you've discovered that Van Dyn thinks that he worked for Capone and that he's the world's worst man and that Truman is still president . . . Just think of Van Dyn as a wrestler, stretched out on the canvas, his wasted muscles nattering at his bones . . . VAN DYN THE SABRE TOOTH IRON MAN . . . rotten eye teeth and another man's thumbstained speciality holds worked from a bicycle battery in his head . . . They classed him with Bert Assirati in nineteen thirty seven.

Anyway, Cafferty, you have now seen the disparity or the parity between the public image and the private face in microcosm, and all that drek.

I suppose so, Cafferty says.

If you have the right combination of brain cells in the left cerebral hemisphere, Lomas goes on, you can sum up all your preoccupations in an epigram and there would be no need for all this.

Is there a need for it? Cafferty says, and where's the epigram?

The public image and the private face, Lomas goes on. Was there any connection between them?

I don't know, Cafferty says.

Was there any difference?

I don't know. They're both forced on people who aren't better provided for.

Like the truth, Lomas says.

Why don't you ask him why he suggested you should become acquainted with these people? Freddie Kilennen says.

I don't know, Cafferty says. What would he say?

He has an excessive admiration for decay, Freddie Kilennen says.

Is that so, Lomas?

Something like that . . . a little more elaborate, but not so profound. It is difficult to abstract finalities from people that you can take photographs of. You know, before the war you could hardly say anything in that park without getting your collar felt. It was very strict.

You told me that I should get to know these people before becoming a speaker, Cafferty says.

I'm sorry, Cafferty, I don't really remember it, it was a long time ago. I think I told you to bear them in mind; you didn't seem to know anybody. Are you going to speak?

No, Cafferty says. I thought of getting a job . . .

Get a chest expander instead dear, Freddie Kilennen says. The National Assistance will pay for it.

Well anyway, Lomas says, it's nice to know that the unemployed still come to Hyde Park.

When are you going to speak, Lomas?

Do you know, I thought of starting again.

Starting again . . . you never began.

I did in a way. More to drink?

*   *   *   *   *

The bar closes. They stand talking in the alleyway and then move down the Edgware Road into the subway and into the park. There is a large group under the trees motionless with few of them interested in working their way to the centre: the space in the eye of the storm. Two men at the fringe feel for each other's hands, unclasp them quickly and walk away towards the lake. The man with a silent message stands on his milk crate across the tarmac. Another man kicks along an oil drum, righting it under the gas-light. He stands on it. Small groups surround them: limbs from an insect's abdomen, tightening and extending.

Mary Davies, one of the park cruisers and aged fifty seven, stands at the gate asking each one that comes in for the time, though her legs bit off more than they could chew years back. She moves towards one of the speakers, and shouts: LANGUAGE IS A CREDIT TO YOU . . . LANGUAGE IS A CREDIT TO YOU.

Lomas stares at her and says that if he had taken advantage of all the sexual opportunities offered to him while he was on the platform, he would be dead now. Aggie wanders into the park with a bunch of carrier bags filled with food to distribute. She leaves them on the tarmac, tucks her hands under the string round her black coat and shouts: PRAISE TO THE LORD, who shall come into your HEARTS, and MINDS and BODIES like a thundering SWORD, and the spirit of FIRE, and shall cast out the devil and all the EVIL . . .

The queers gather round her and ask her: What about sex on the hire purchase because of the high price of low living, and Where are the brakes on a ship, and Where are the droppings from an aeroplane. Aggie blesses them, clutches them and asks the Lord to take this sin from them. They tear away from her and run round her squawking, like chickens with broken necks. Aggie leaves, keeps her breath for sowing dandelions.

He's mouthing, Cafferty says.
Who?
The man with the silent message.
He's speaking, Lomas says. Very curious. He said to me earlier on that if he ever went over to the park and spoke, nothing would be so profound as the fact that he was there. Let's move.

They walk across the tarmac and stand beneath his milk crate.

I think it is very important to distinguish, the man with the silent message is saying, to distinguish between what is rational and what is irrational. Suppose I were to say that at a given point in time, the point being donated by a charitable pin (he laughs), I MIGHT say something more intelligent than Socrates; that is a hypothesis and therefore has the touch of rationality.

But if I were to say that at a given point in time, the point again being donated by a charitable pin (he laughs), I am DEFINITELY going to say something more intelligent than Socrates . . . although I may WELL say something more intelligent than Socrates at that given point in time (he laughs) and although the hypothesis that I conceived about my POSSIBLY saying something more intelligent than Socrates at a given point in time (he smiles), proceeded from an ILLUSORY idea of my own that I COULD say something more intelligent than Socrates . . . this last, and not the former, has the touch of irrationality. . . .

Dishevelled coherency, that's the way the money goes, Lomas says and he looks up at the man with the silent message. Why have you decided to speak?

Still waters runneth deep, dear, says Freddie Kilennen.

They have stronger bladders, that is all, Cafferty says. If the man with the silent message has decided to open his mouth, it's time you spoke, Lomas. It's time you broke the silence.

Spoke?

Spoke, says Freddie Kilennen, and they lead him over to a park chair behind the refreshment stall. A man at the fringe of the large crowd under the trees watches Lomas in an opportunist way.

Lomas stands by the chair with his hands in his raincoat pockets. He lifts one foot onto the chair.

The Minister for the Postponements of Accidents, says Freddie Kilennen.

The ghost that goes for anything in sheets, says Cafferty.

Lomas opens his mouth slowly; a thin film of spit slides to the corners of his lips.

Few theologians would agree, Lomas says, but one side of a coin is the same size as the other . . .

He pauses, stares at the chair, takes stock of the height, remembers all the jokes about being on a platform: that it raises you above the level of the common herd, and that only when you're on a platform or your shoes wear out are you standing on your own two feet, and that you only stood on it to look out for a friend, and wonders whether they were jokes, and wonders whether that was how they went and goes on:

There is too much tension in jokes. I must give them up. . . .

Well done, Cafferty says. You are now part of the small psychosis on weekly sale to the tourists.

So are you . . .

Stand on the PLATFORM, will you? pretentious old bastard, says Freddie Kilennen.

Lomas bends down to the foot he is resting on the clinker part of the seat, unties the shoe lace, and reties it in a double knot.

I remember Bonar Thompson saying to me, Lomas goes on, staring at his shoe on the chair, it was after one of his meetings in the thirties, and he said to me that the physical effort of speaking stirred up the brain and caused thoughts to emerge from their hiding place in the subconscious. I didn't believe him then and I don't now.

Lomas takes his foot off the chair.

Why couldn't you have said that on the platform? Freddie Kilennen says.

And speaking, Lomas says, ignoring him, speaking is supposed to have an effect on the glucose supply leading to your brain. I think I must have an impaired glucose tolerance . . . spiritually diabetic. But I suppose it could give you quite a warm feeling . . . quite a warm feeling.

The implication of your not standing on that chair, Cafferty says, is that there is some merit in standing on a platform.

No, Lomas says. There is only merit as regards myself.

*   *   *   *   *

They move to the mirrored section of Fortes, and Lomas stares at himself in the mirrors, and Freddie Kilennen pours whisky into his tea.

These people, Lomas says slowly, these people are a dustbin myth preserved by the administrators, who come to the park from time to time, when there's a war on, or a strike, to see that the right sort of free speech is spoken there, put it in the tourist guides, take a few pictures of the speakers in emphatic positions to show to their children and to laugh at. . . . Caked carnation sap behind their lapels. But their world Cafferty, is within spitting distance of all the tatterdam trash in that park, and yet the place breeds arrogance, and they go away supercilious. But when they've been listening . . . when they've been listening, they've stared at the speakers agape . . . like a urinal.

Lomas has a lovely graveside manner, Freddie Kilennen says. It WAS like that, Cafferty, it was like that before the war, and he misses it being like that now. That's what he's on about.

You don't remember the war, do you Cafferty, Lomas says. Babies on the bomb sites with frosted thumbs . . . that was the time to have a harvest festival . . .

For CHRIST'S SAKE, shut your face, Freddie Kilennen says, and stops pouring whisky into his tea. Stupid old fool.

And before the war, Lomas goes on, before the war, we had REAL speakers. ORATORY it was then Cafferty, oratory. . . .

It wasn't at all, Cafferty, says Freddie Kilennen, it was the same jumped up idiots, only they had a fake parliamentary manner: vaseline vowels and three syllables for the price of one.

They had DIGNITY, Lomas says turning to Cafferty from his own reflection. You think some of them have dignity now, and then you look at them more closely . . . It's dull frustration, or post-coital depression, or that mad tone of voice which people use when they speak with authority. There are so many people now, Cafferty, so many ignorant, illogical, boring people forced to register their private decay. . . .

And he's loved every putrefying moment of it, for the last thirty years, Cafferty, for the last thirty years.

You've been coming up here for ten of them, Freddie, Cafferty says. Why?

Do you mean to say you don't know? Lomas says. You don't know? Freddie was on the plating stakes before Mary Pickford was born . . . pushing a bit of the other, and now he wanders round the park half the night trying to get it back. That was what he was doing when you met him, wasn't it?

I suppose so, Cafferty says.

Ah shut your face, says Freddie Kilennen, you're in it for nothing I suppose, Lomas? We'll go back to the park.

They cross the road, enter Cumberland Gate. The groups are still there. The man on the *Catholic Evidence Guild* platform closes down the meeting and says that there is a meeting every night of the week except Tuesday, so that if his listeners know nothing about the *Catholic Evidence Guild*, it is their fault and not his, and Lomas says that reason is an emotion for the sexless.

A few people wander from group to group, renewing their licence for saying the same things over and over again.

Mary Davies goes back alone to the North End Road. Harry goes back to Chiswick. Norman goes back to Shepherds Bush.

Two policemen stand under the gas lamp. One of them is sucking his helmet strap. Lomas stares at them, and observes that they travel in pairs because they are neurotic. If they travelled alone, they would start talking to themselves.

One of the policemen looks at his watch. They lock one gate and herd the people towards the other.

They want us to go, Lomas says. There are so many people forced to register their private decay . . . so many ritual aspirations . . . so many voices pretending to be everybody's womb . . . They want us to go, Cafferty. I quite like it here.

*   *   *   *   *

The park gates are bolted. The police leave. Van Dyn has stomped all the cardboard cups. The litter bins are full. A fog wreathes over the tarmac. Objectivity is the first and last stage of any disease.